Table of Contents

Decimals

Percents

USING NUMBER POWER — 133

To the Student

Welcome to *Fractions, Decimals, and Percents:*
Number Power 2 is designed to help you build and use the fraction, decimal, and percent skills found in the workplace and everyday experiences. This books extends the whole number skills developed in *Number Power 1*.

The first section of the book, Building Number Power, provides easy-to-follow instructions and plenty of practice working with fractions, decimals, and percents. Each chapter begins with a skills inventory so that you can evaluate your strengths and weaknesses and ends with a review so that you can measure your progress.

Scattered throughout the book are tips on using a calculator, estimating answers, and solving problems with mental math shortcuts. The following icons will alert you to the problems where using these skills will be especially helpful.

 calculator icon

estimation icon

mental math icon

The second section of the book, Using Number Power, gives you an opportunity to use your math skills to solve real-life problems.

At the back of the book is an answer key for all the exercises and tests. Checking the answer key after you work through a lesson will help you measure your progress. Also included in the back are quick reference pages for using a calculator, estimation, and mental math. Refer to these pages for a quick review and helpful explanation. Inside the back cover is a chart to help you keep track of your score on each exercise.

After carefully working through *Number Power 2,* you will be able to handle the fractions, decimals, and percents needed in daily living, in school, and on many standardized tests, including the GED. The skills you develop will give you a solid foundation for your increasing number power.

Pretest

This test will tell you which sections of *Number Power 2* you need to concentrate on. Do every problem that you can. Correct answers are listed by page number at the back of the book. After you check your answers, the chart at the end of the test will guide you to the pages of the book where you need work.

1. Reduce $\frac{18}{24}$ to the lowest terms.

2. $2\frac{3}{4} + 4\frac{5}{6} + 1\frac{3}{8} =$

3. Is the sum of $\frac{4}{7} + \frac{8}{15}$ greater than 1, less than 1, or equal to 1?

4. The base of a kitchen counter is $34\frac{1}{4}$ inches high. The counter, which rests on the base, is $1\frac{7}{8}$ inches thick. Find the height of the counter.

5. $12\frac{3}{10} - 7\frac{2}{3} =$

6. From a 5-pound bag of flour, Maura used $2\frac{3}{16}$ pounds to bake cakes. Find the weight of the flour left in the bag.

7. $\frac{5}{8} \times \frac{4}{9} =$

8. $2\frac{2}{3} \times 1\frac{3}{4} \times 7\frac{1}{2} =$

9. In the problem $2\frac{7}{8} \times 5\frac{1}{6}$, first round each number to the nearest whole number. Then multiply.

10. Because of snow, Mavis's evening Spanish class was canceled. The next week $\frac{2}{3}$ of the 24 students in the class agreed to have a make-up class. How many students wanted the make-up class?

11. $4\frac{1}{2} \div 9 =$

12. $3\frac{1}{4} \div 1\frac{1}{8} =$

13. Jake cut a pipe that was $17\frac{1}{2}$ inches long into five equal pieces. Assuming there was no waste, how long was each piece?

14. On a Spanish vocabulary quiz, Connie got $\frac{3}{4}$ of the words right. She answered 36 words correctly. How many words were on the quiz?

15. Write twelve and sixteen thousandths as a mixed decimal.

16. Write the following decimals in order from smallest to largest: 0.057, 0.7, 0.075, 0.57

17. $5.63 + 12 + 1.078 =$

18. A carpenter attached a metal cover that was 0.125 inch thick onto a board that was 1.5 inches thick. Find the combined thickness of the board and the cover.

19. $2.8 - 1.097 =$

20. In the problem 8.37 − 1.629, first round each number to the nearest tenth. Then subtract.

21. The area of Washington, D.C., is 62.7 square miles. The area of nearby Baltimorc is 80.3 square miles. The area of Baltimore is how much larger than the area of Washington, D.C.?

22. $4.07 \times 2.6 =$

23. In the problem 89.6×0.78, first round 89.6 to the nearest *ten* and round 0.78 to the nearest *tenth*. Then multiply.

24. To the nearest penny, what is the price of 3.2 pounds of ham that costs $2.99 per pound?

25. $11.02 \div 2.9 =$

26. $90 \div 0.45 =$

27. Find the answer to $8.8 \div 0.7$ to the nearest tenth.

28. Three crates weigh a total of 128.6 pounds. To the nearest tenth, what is the average weight of each crate?

29. Write 4.8% as a decimal.

30. Write $\frac{5}{12}$ as a percent.

31. Write $6\frac{1}{4}\%$ as a fraction in lowest terms.

32. Find 27% of 300.

33. Find $12\frac{1}{2}\%$ of 48.

34. Which of the following is the same as 20% of 75?

    a. $75 \div 2$ **c.** $75 \div 4$
    b. $75 \div 3$ **d.** $75 \div 5$

35. Iris works in the quality control department of a factory that makes children's clothes. In a week when the factory produced 350 items, Iris found 4% of them to be defective. How many clothing items were defective that week?

36. The attendance on opening night of a county fair was 2,400 people. The attendance on the last night of the fair was 15% more than the opening night. Find the attendance for the last night of the fair.

37. 84 is what percent of 112?

38. John wants to buy an outdoor grill that costs $400. So far he has saved $250. What percent of the cost of the grill has he saved?

39. When a home delivery meal service started, they prepared and delivered 320 meals. One year later the service was delivering 576 meals. By what percent did the number of meals increase?

40. In December Yanni's Chocolate Shop received 180 telephone orders. In January they received only 72 telephone orders. By what percent did the number of telephone orders decrease from December to January?

41. 60% of what number is 72?

42. On a flight to Chicago, there were 104 occupied seats. The occupied seats represent 80% of the total number of seats on the plane. How many seats are on the plane?

43. The road crew in the village of Pleasant Hill hopes to have every street in the village resurfaced by the end of October. By the first of October the crew had resurfaced 36 streets which represent 75% of the total. How many streets are there in Pleasant Hill?

Pretest Chart

If you miss more than one problem in any section of this test, you should complete the lessons on the practice pages indicated on this chart. If you miss only one problem in a section of a test, you may not need further study in that section. However, before you skip those lessons, we recommend that you complete the review test at the end of that chapter. For example, if you miss one problem about fractions, you should pass the Fractions Review (page 58) before beginning the chapter on decimals. This longer inventory will be a more precise indicator of your skill level.

PROBLEM NUMBERS	SKILL AREA	PRACTICE PAGES
1, 2, 3, 4	understanding and adding fractions	11–30
5, 6	subtracting fractions	31–38
7, 8, 9	multiplying fractions	39–46
10, 11, 12, 13, 14	dividing fractions	47–57
15, 16, 17, 18	understanding and adding decimals	62–74
19, 20, 21	subtracting decimals	75–78
22, 23, 24	multiplying decimals	79–85
25, 26, 27, 28	dividing decimals	86–93
29, 30, 31	understanding percent	98–103
32, 33, 34, 35, 36	finding a percent	104–109
37, 38, 39, 40	finding what percent one number is of another	110–113
41, 42, 43	finding a number when a percent is given	115–118

Building
Number
Power

FRACTIONS

Fraction Skills Inventory

This inventory will tell you whether you need to work through the fractions section of *Number Power 2*. Do all the problems that you can. There is no time limit. Work carefully and check your answers, but do not use outside help. Correct answers are listed by page number at the back of the book.

1. A pound contains 16 ounces. 10 ounces is what fraction of a pound?

2. Which fractions in this list are greater than $\frac{1}{2}$? $\frac{5}{6}, \frac{4}{8}, \frac{3}{4}, \frac{9}{20}$

3. Reduce $\frac{28}{42}$ to lowest terms.

4. Write $\frac{24}{10}$ as a mixed number.

5. Write $5\frac{3}{7}$ as an improper fraction.

6. Change $\frac{2}{3}$ to eighteenths.

7. $3\frac{11}{15} + 4\frac{7}{15} =$

8. $3\frac{1}{3} + 2\frac{3}{4} + 5\frac{5}{6} =$

9. Without finding the exact sum, tell whether $\frac{5}{12} + \frac{1}{2}$ is less than 1, greater than 1, or equal to 1.

10. A wooden crate weighing $2\frac{5}{16}$ pounds contains grapefruit weighing $24\frac{1}{2}$ pounds. What is the combined weight of the crate and the grapefruit?

11. Fred is a traveling salesman. He spent $1\frac{3}{4}$ hours driving on Monday, $2\frac{1}{3}$ hours driving on Tuesday, and $2\frac{1}{6}$ hours driving on Wednesday. Find the total number of hours he drove those three days.

12. $12\frac{3}{4} - 6\frac{2}{5} =$

13. $9\frac{1}{8} - 4\frac{5}{8} =$

14. $10\frac{2}{7} - 6\frac{2}{3} =$

15. Maxine weighed 135 pounds. By dieting she lost $10\frac{1}{2}$ pounds. How much did she weigh after her diet?

16. From a piece of cloth $42\frac{1}{4}$ inches long, Celeste cut a strip $14\frac{3}{4}$ inches long. How long was the remaining piece?

17. $\frac{7}{10} \times \frac{3}{4} =$

18. $\frac{3}{5} \times \frac{10}{21} \times \frac{7}{8} =$

19. $2\frac{2}{5} \times 6\frac{1}{4} =$

20. In the problem $1\frac{3}{5} \times 3\frac{1}{4}$, round each number to the nearest whole number. Then multiply.

21. Bill shipped $\frac{7}{10}$ of the crates in his warehouse by air freight. If there were 40 crates in the warehouse, how many did he ship?

22. Gloria works $7\frac{1}{2}$ hours a day. How many hours does she work in a 5-day work week?

23. $\frac{5}{8} \div \frac{9}{16} =$

24. $12 \div \frac{3}{4} =$

25. $\frac{7}{9} \div 14 =$

26. $3\frac{3}{4} \div 1\frac{5}{7} =$

27. $\frac{3}{4}$ of what number is 36?

28. How many $\frac{1}{2}$-pound bags can be filled with 14 pounds of peanuts?

29. From a strip of wood 125 inches long, George is cutting pieces $12\frac{1}{2}$ inches long. How many pieces can he cut from the long strip?

Fraction Skills Inventory Chart

If you missed more than one problem in any group below, work through the practice pages for that group. Then redo the problems you got wrong on the Fraction Skills Inventory. If you had a passing score on all five groups of problems, redo any problem you missed and begin the Decimal Skills Inventory on page 60.

PROBLEM NUMBERS	SKILL AREA	PRACTICE PAGES
1, 2, 3, 4, 5, 6	understanding fractions	11–21
7, 8, 9, 10, 11	adding fractions	22–30
12, 13, 14, 15, 16	subtracting fractions	31–38
17, 18, 19, 20, 21, 22	multiplying fractions	39–46
23, 24, 25, 26, 27, 28, 29	dividing fractions	47–57

Understanding Fractions

A **fraction** is a part of a whole. A penny is a fraction of a dollar. It is one of the 100 equal parts of a dollar or $\frac{1}{100}$ (one hundred*th*) of a dollar. An inch is a fraction of a foot. It is one of the 12 equal parts of a foot or $\frac{1}{12}$ (one twelf*th*) of a foot. 5 days are a fraction of a week. They are 5 of the 7 equal parts of a week or $\frac{5}{7}$ (five seven*ths*) of a week.

The two numbers in a fraction are called the **numerator** and the **denominator.**

$\dfrac{\textbf{numerator}}{\textbf{denominator}}$ tells how many parts you have
 tells how many parts in the whole

<u>EXAMPLE</u> The fraction $\frac{3}{4}$ tells you what part of the figure at the right is shaded. 3 parts are shaded. The whole figure is divided into 4 equal parts.

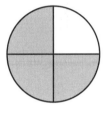

Write fractions that represent the part of each figure that is shaded.

1.

2.

3.

4.

5.

6.

7.

8.

9.
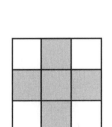

Writing Fractions

Since there are three feet in one yard, one foot is $\frac{1}{3}$ of a yard. Two feet make up $\frac{2}{3}$ of a yard.

Write fractions for each of the *parts* described below.

1. A foot contains 12 inches. 5 inches is what fraction of a foot?

2. 47¢ is what fraction of a dollar?

3. A pound contains 16 ounces. 9 ounces is what fraction of a pound?

4. A yard contains 36 inches. 23 inches is what fraction of a yard?

5. 7 months is what fraction of a year?

6. 8¢ is what fraction of a quarter?

7. Earlene wants a jacket that costs $60. She has saved $43. What fraction of the amount that she needs has she saved?

8. There are 2,000 pounds in a ton. 1,351 pounds is what fraction of a ton?

9. During a 5-day work week, Pete was sick for 2 days. What fraction of the work week was he sick?

10. There are 100 centimeters in a meter. 63 centimeters is what fraction of a meter?

11. There are 4 quarts in a gallon. 3 quarts is what fraction of a gallon?

12. David makes $350 a week. He has spent $113. What fraction of his week's pay has he spent?

13. Madge has typed 77 pages of a report that contains 280 pages. What fraction of the report has she typed?

Identifying Forms of Fractions

In a **proper fraction,** the top number is *less than* the bottom number.

EXAMPLES $\frac{1}{3}, \frac{3}{10}, \frac{7}{19}$

A proper fraction is less than all the parts the whole is divided into. The value of a proper fraction is *always less than one.*

In an **improper fraction,** the top number is *equal to or larger than* the bottom number.

EXAMPLES $\frac{3}{2}, \frac{9}{4}, \frac{8}{8}$

An improper fraction is all the parts that a whole is divided into such as $\frac{8}{8}$, or it is more than the total parts in the whole. The value of an improper fraction is either equal to one or more than one.

In a **mixed number,** a whole number is written next to a proper fraction.

EXAMPLES $1\frac{2}{5}, 3\frac{1}{2}, 10\frac{4}{7}$

Tell whether each of the following is a proper fraction (P), an improper fraction (I), or a mixed number (M).

1. $\frac{9}{6}$ $\qquad$ $\frac{8}{30}$ $\qquad$ $4\frac{1}{2}$ $\qquad$ $\frac{10}{10}$

2. $\frac{15}{16}$ $\qquad$ $\frac{20}{19}$ $\qquad$ $\frac{17}{17}$ $\qquad$ $12\frac{1}{10}$

3. $9\frac{2}{7}$ $\qquad$ $\frac{55}{100}$ $\qquad$ $\frac{2}{200}$ $\qquad$ $\frac{200}{2}$

4. $\frac{75}{110}$ $\qquad$ $\frac{110}{75}$ $\qquad$ $1\frac{8}{9}$ $\qquad$ $\frac{8}{50}$

Thinking About the Size of Fractions

In a proper fraction, the **numerator** (top number) is less than the **denominator** (bottom number). The size of the numerator *compared* to the size of the denominator tells you something about the size of the fraction.

> A fraction is equal to one-half when the numerator is exactly half of the denominator.

EXAMPLES The fractions $\frac{2}{4}$, $\frac{5}{10}$, and $\frac{15}{30}$ are each equal to one-half.

1. Circle the fractions that are *equal to* $\frac{1}{2}$ in the following list.

$$\frac{4}{9} \qquad \frac{6}{12} \qquad \frac{9}{18} \qquad \frac{7}{15} \qquad \frac{3}{7} \qquad \frac{8}{16} \qquad \frac{12}{24}$$

> A fraction is less than one-half when the numerator is less than half of the denominator.

EXAMPLES The fractions $\frac{1}{3}$, $\frac{2}{5}$, and $\frac{12}{50}$ are each less than one-half.

2. Circle the fractions that are *less than* $\frac{1}{2}$ in the following list.

$$\frac{2}{7} \qquad \frac{3}{8} \qquad \frac{6}{12} \qquad \frac{9}{10} \qquad \frac{4}{9} \qquad \frac{9}{20} \qquad \frac{4}{15}$$

> A fraction is greater than one-half when the numerator is more than half of the denominator.

EXAMPLES The fractions $\frac{3}{5}$, $\frac{7}{10}$, and $\frac{24}{35}$ are each greater than one-half.

3. Circle the fractions that are *greater than* $\frac{1}{2}$ in the following list.

$$\frac{3}{4} \qquad \frac{3}{6} \qquad \frac{7}{8} \qquad \frac{9}{15} \qquad \frac{8}{12} \qquad \frac{10}{20} \qquad \frac{17}{30}$$

The symbol = means "is equal to." $\qquad \frac{12}{24} = \frac{1}{2}$ because 12 is half of 24.

The symbol < means "is less than." $\qquad \frac{5}{14} < \frac{1}{2}$ because 5 is less than half of 14.

The symbol > means "is greater than." $\qquad \frac{9}{10} > \frac{1}{2}$ because 9 is more than half of 10.

In the box between each pair of fractions, write a symbol that makes the statement true. The first problem is done as an example.

4. $\frac{3}{5} \boxed{>} \frac{1}{2}$ $\qquad\qquad$ $\frac{8}{16} \square \frac{1}{2}$ $\qquad\qquad$ $\frac{7}{20} \square \frac{1}{2}$ $\qquad\qquad$ $\frac{9}{15} \square \frac{1}{2}$

Reducing Fractions

A quarter (25¢) represents 25 pennies out of the total of 100 pennies in a dollar. A quarter is $\frac{25}{100}$ of a dollar. A quarter also equals five nickels out of the total of 20 nickels in a dollar. A quarter is $\frac{5}{20}$ of a dollar. A quarter is also one of the four equal parts of a dollar or $\frac{1}{4}$ of a dollar. The fraction $\frac{1}{4}$ is the *reduced* form of both $\frac{25}{100}$ and $\frac{5}{20}$.

Reducing a fraction means writing the fraction with smaller numbers without changing the value of the fraction. Study the following examples to see how fractions are reduced.

EXAMPLE 1 Reduce $\frac{15}{20}$.

STEP 1 Find a number that divides evenly into both the numerator and the denominator. 5 divides evenly into both 15 and 20.

$$\frac{15 \div 5}{20 \div 5} = \frac{3}{4}$$

STEP 2 Check to see if another number divides evenly into both 3 and 4. Since no other number besides 1 divides evenly into 3 and 4, the fraction is reduced as far as it will go.

EXAMPLE 2 Reduce $\frac{32}{64}$.

STEP 1 Find a number that divides evenly into both the numerator and the denominator. 8 divides evenly into both 32 and 64.

$$\frac{32 \div 8}{64 \div 8} = \frac{4}{8}$$

STEP 2 Check to see if another number divides evenly into both 4 and 8. 4 divides evenly into both 4 and 8.

$$\frac{4 \div 4}{8 \div 4} = \frac{1}{2}$$

STEP 3 Check to see if another number divides evenly into both 1 and 2. Since no other number besides 1 divides evenly into 1 and 2, the fraction is reduced as far as it will go.

When you reduce a fraction, the *value* of the fraction does not change. A reduced fraction is *equal to* the original fraction. For example, $\frac{32}{64} = \frac{1}{2}$. When a fraction is reduced as much as possible, the fraction is reduced to **lowest terms.**

When both the numerator and the denominator of a fraction end with zeros, you can cancel the zeros one-for-one. This is a shortcut for reducing by ten. Always check to see if you can continue to reduce.

EXAMPLE 3 Reduce $\frac{20}{30}$ to lowest terms.

    STEP 1 Cancel the zeros one-for-one.

$$\frac{2\cancel{0}}{3\cancel{0}}$$

    STEP 2 Check to see if you can continue to reduce.

              The fraction $\frac{2}{3}$ is reduced to lowest terms.

$$\frac{2}{3}$$

EXAMPLE 4 Reduce $\frac{40}{100}$ to lowest terms.

    STEP 1 Cancel the zeros one-for-one. Be sure to cancel only one zero in the denominator since you canceled only one zero in the numerator.

$$\frac{4\cancel{0}}{10\cancel{0}}$$

    STEP 2 Check to see if you can continue to reduce. Divide both 4 and 10 by 2.

$$\frac{4 \div 2}{10 \div 2} = \frac{2}{5}$$

....

Reduce each fraction to lowest terms.

1. $\frac{6}{12} =$ $\frac{7}{28} =$ $\frac{3}{9} =$ $\frac{9}{45} =$ $\frac{6}{48} =$

2. $\frac{25}{30} =$ $\frac{32}{36} =$ $\frac{16}{18} =$ $\frac{21}{24} =$ $\frac{14}{21} =$

3. $\frac{20}{50} =$ $\frac{30}{90} =$ $\frac{70}{200} =$ $\frac{90}{140} =$ $\frac{80}{170} =$

4. $\frac{33}{77} =$ $\frac{45}{60} =$ $\frac{18}{36} =$ $\frac{42}{56} =$ $\frac{48}{64} =$

5. $\frac{75}{80} =$ $\frac{420}{480} =$ $\frac{72}{90} =$ $\frac{26}{39} =$ $\frac{18}{32} =$

6. $\frac{25}{50} =$ $\frac{14}{42} =$ $\frac{4}{200} =$ $\frac{63}{81} =$ $\frac{35}{49} =$

For each problem, write a fraction. Then reduce.

7. Eight inches is what fraction of a foot? (1 foot = 12 inches)

8. Sally has saved $1,200 for a used car that costs $2,000. What fraction of the total price has she saved?

9. Sam gets 15 vacation days each year. By June 1, Sam had used six of his vacation days. What fraction of the year's total did he use so far?

10. In spring Max weighed 200 pounds. Over the summer he lost 20 pounds. What fraction of his weight did he lose?

11. Ten ounces is what fraction of a pound? (1 pound = 16 ounces)

12. There are 21 students in Monica's math class. Fourteen of the students are women. Women make up what fraction of the class?

13. For the class in problem 12, what fraction of the students are men?

14. On a quiz with 12 problems, Evelyn got 3 problems wrong. What fraction of the problems did she get wrong?

15. For the quiz in problem 14, what fraction of the problems did Evelyn get right?

16. The distance from Sam's house to his job is 16 miles. On his way to work each morning, Sam drops his daughter off at school. The school is 2 miles from their house. What fraction of the total drive to his job has Sam completed when he drops off his daughter?

17. Sheila has to type a 36-page report. When she took her coffee break, she had already typed 20 pages of the report. What fraction of the whole report has she typed?

18. For the last problem, what fraction of the report does Sheila have left to type when she comes back from her coffee break?

19. The Westside Community Center needs $24,000 for their summer youth program. So far they have raised $15,000. What fraction of the total cost have they raised?

20. For the last problem, what fraction of the cost of the summer youth program does the community center need to raise?

Raising Fractions to Higher Terms

An important skill in the addition and subtraction of fractions is raising a fraction to **higher terms.** This is the opposite of reducing a fraction. To reduce a fraction, you must *divide* both the numerator and the denominator by the same number. To raise a fraction to higher terms, *multiply* both the numerator and the denominator by the same number.

EXAMPLE 1 Raise $\frac{2}{5}$ to a new fraction with a denominator of 20.

STEP 1	Divide the old denominator into the new one. The new denominator is 4 times the old one.	$20 \div 5 = 4$
STEP 2	Since the new denominator is 4 times the old one, multiply the old numerator by 4.	$\frac{2 \times 4}{5 \times 4} = \frac{8}{20}$
	To check the answer, divide 8 and 20 by 4.	$\frac{8 \div 4}{20 \div 4} = \frac{2}{5}$

EXAMPLE 2 $\frac{4}{9} = \frac{?}{27}$

STEP 1	Divide the old denominator into the new one. The new denominator is 3 times the old one.	$27 \div 9 = 3$
STEP 2	Since the new denominator is 3 times the old one, multiply the old numerator by 3.	$\frac{4 \times 3}{9 \times 3} = \frac{12}{27}$
	To check the answer, divide 12 and 27 by 3.	$\frac{12 \div 3}{27 \div 3} = \frac{4}{9}$

Raise each fraction to higher terms by filling in the missing numerator.

1. $\frac{4}{5} = \frac{}{30}$ $\frac{9}{10} = \frac{}{20}$ $\frac{1}{6} = \frac{}{18}$ $\frac{5}{8} = \frac{}{32}$

2. $\frac{4}{7} = \frac{}{35}$ $\frac{1}{2} = \frac{}{36}$ $\frac{2}{3} = \frac{}{21}$ $\frac{9}{11} = \frac{}{66}$

3. $\frac{5}{9} = \frac{}{45}$ $\frac{3}{4} = \frac{}{44}$ $\frac{7}{12} = \frac{}{60}$ $\frac{1}{3} = \frac{}{45}$

4. $\frac{1}{2} = \frac{}{50}$ $\frac{3}{8} = \frac{}{40}$ $\frac{2}{9} = \frac{}{72}$ $\frac{5}{6} = \frac{}{42}$

Changing Improper Fractions to Whole or Mixed Numbers

Earlier you learned that a fraction is a part of a whole. The fraction $\frac{3}{4}$ means a whole is divided into four parts and you have three of those parts.

You can also think of a fraction as a division problem The fraction bar (−) or the slash (/) mean to divide. The fraction $\frac{3}{4}$ can mean *three divided by four.* You will learn more about dividing proper fractions when you study decimals.

The improper fraction $\frac{8}{8}$ means *eight divided by eight.*

EXAMPLE 1   Change $\frac{8}{8}$ to a whole number.

Divide 8 by 8.

$$\frac{8}{8} = 8\overline{)8}^{\,\mathbf{1}}$$

EXAMPLE 2   Change $\frac{20}{4}$ to a whole number.

Divide 20 by 4.

$$\frac{20}{4} = 4\overline{)20}^{\,\mathbf{5}}$$

When there is a remainder, write a fraction with the remainder over the denominator. The result is a mixed number.

EXAMPLE 3   Change $\frac{21}{9}$ to a mixed number.

    STEP 1   Divide 21 by 9.

    STEP 2   Write the remainder, 3, over the denominator, 9.

    STEP 3   Reduce $\frac{3}{9}$ by dividing 3 and 9 by 3.

$$9\overline{)21}^{\,2\frac{3}{9}}$$
$$\underline{18}$$
$$3$$

$$\frac{3 \div 3}{9 \div 3} = \frac{1}{3}$$

ANSWER: $2\frac{1}{3}$

For the last example, you can reduce the improper fraction before you change it to a mixed number. The result will be the same.

$$\frac{21 \div 3}{9 \div 3} = \frac{7}{3} \qquad 3\overline{)7}^{\,2\frac{1}{3}}$$

Division word problems can be written as improper fractions. Remember that the amount being divided comes on top, and the divisor goes on the bottom.

EXAMPLE 4   A kitchen counter is 90 inches long. Find the length of the
counter in feet. (1 foot = 12 inches)

STEP 1   Write the problem as an improper fraction. Divide $\dfrac{90}{12}$
90 inches by the number of inches in one foot.

STEP 2   Divide 90 by 12.

$$12\overline{)90}^{\,7\frac{6}{12}}$$

STEP 3   Reduce $\dfrac{6}{12}$ by dividing 6 and 12 by 6. $\dfrac{6 \div 6}{12 \div 6} = \dfrac{1}{2}$

ANSWER: $7\dfrac{1}{2}$

....

**Change each fraction to a whole number or a mixed number.
Reduce any remaining fractions.**

1. $\dfrac{14}{8} =$ $\qquad$ $\dfrac{33}{6} =$ $\qquad$ $\dfrac{14}{5} =$ $\qquad$ $\dfrac{30}{7} =$ $\qquad$ $\dfrac{12}{3} =$

2. $\dfrac{30}{9} =$ $\qquad$ $\dfrac{26}{8} =$ $\qquad$ $\dfrac{18}{6} =$ $\qquad$ $\dfrac{36}{10} =$ $\qquad$ $\dfrac{16}{8} =$

3. $\dfrac{13}{12} =$ $\qquad$ $\dfrac{45}{9} =$ $\qquad$ $\dfrac{45}{6} =$ $\qquad$ $\dfrac{32}{12} =$ $\qquad$ $\dfrac{42}{9} =$

4. $\dfrac{36}{12} =$ $\qquad$ $\dfrac{28}{10} =$ $\qquad$ $\dfrac{11}{2} =$ $\qquad$ $\dfrac{44}{16} =$ $\qquad$ $\dfrac{50}{4} =$

**Write the next division problems as improper fractions. Then change
the improper fractions to mixed numbers. Reduce any remaining
fractions.**

5. It took Mrs. Pagan 100 minutes to drive to the nearest shopping
center. Change the time to hours. (1 hour = 60 minutes)

6. Steve cut a board 8 feet long into three equal pieces. How long was
each piece?

7. An elevator can carry a load of 2,500 pounds. How many tons can
it carry? (1 ton = 2,000 pounds)

8. In a school where adult education classes are held, each classroom
can hold 30 students. How many classrooms are needed for
255 students?

Changing Mixed Numbers to Improper Fractions

An important skill in multiplication and division of fractions is changing a mixed number, such as $2\frac{1}{4}$, to an improper fraction. You know that one whole equals $\frac{4}{4}$ and that 2 equals $\frac{8}{4}$. Adding the extra $\frac{1}{4}$, you get $\frac{9}{4}$.

$$\frac{4}{4} + \frac{4}{4} + \frac{1}{4} = \frac{9}{4}$$

Study the next examples to see how to change mixed numbers to improper fractions.

EXAMPLE 1 Change $2\frac{1}{4}$ to an improper fraction.

STEP 1 Multiply the denominator, 4, by the whole number, 2. $4 \times 2 = 8$

STEP 2 Add the numerator, 1, to 8. $8 + 1 = 9$

STEP 3 Write the total, 9, over the denominator, 4. $2\frac{1}{4} = \frac{9}{4}$

EXAMPLE 2 Change $5\frac{2}{3}$ to an improper fraction.

STEP 1 Multiply the denominator, 3, by the whole number, 5. $3 \times 5 = 15$

STEP 2 Add the numerator, 2, to 15. $15 + 2 = 17$

STEP 3 Write the total, 17, over the denominator, 3. $5\frac{2}{3} = \frac{17}{3}$

Change each mixed number to an improper fraction.

1. $2\frac{3}{4} =$ $1\frac{4}{7} =$ $5\frac{1}{3} =$ $6\frac{2}{7} =$ $4\frac{3}{5} =$

2. $9\frac{1}{2} =$ $7\frac{5}{8} =$ $2\frac{9}{10} =$ $8\frac{3}{4} =$ $3\frac{5}{9} =$

3. $10\frac{1}{3} =$ $11\frac{2}{5} =$ $4\frac{5}{12} =$ $6\frac{7}{8} =$ $12\frac{1}{4} =$

4. $3\frac{4}{5} =$ $6\frac{1}{7} =$ $9\frac{3}{8} =$ $2\frac{1}{12} =$ $5\frac{4}{15} =$

Adding Fractions with the Same Denominators

The answer to an addition problem is called the **sum** or **total.** You know that the sum of a quarter and another quarter is two quarters, or $\frac{1}{2}$ dollar.

To add fractions with the same denominators, add the numerators, and put the total over the denominator.

EXAMPLE $\quad \frac{2}{7} + \frac{3}{7} =$

$$\begin{array}{r} \frac{2}{7} \\ + \frac{3}{7} \\ \hline \frac{5}{7} \end{array}$$

STEP 1 Add the numerators. $2 + 3 = 5$

STEP 2 Put the total, 5, over the denominator 7.

Add.

1. $\quad \frac{2}{9}$ $\qquad \frac{3}{7}$ $\qquad \frac{4}{8}$ $\qquad \frac{5}{12}$ $\qquad \frac{4}{13}$

 $\quad + \frac{3}{9}$ $\qquad + \frac{1}{7}$ $\qquad + \frac{3}{8}$ $\qquad + \frac{2}{12}$ $\qquad + \frac{6}{13}$

2. $\quad \frac{3}{11}$ $\qquad \frac{5}{9}$ $\qquad \frac{2}{15}$ $\qquad \frac{8}{17}$ $\qquad \frac{2}{19}$

 $\quad \frac{1}{11}$ $\qquad \frac{2}{9}$ $\qquad \frac{7}{15}$ $\qquad \frac{2}{17}$ $\qquad \frac{9}{19}$

 $\quad + \frac{2}{11}$ $\qquad + \frac{1}{9}$ $\qquad + \frac{4}{15}$ $\qquad + \frac{5}{17}$ $\qquad + \frac{5}{19}$

With mixed numbers, add fractions and whole numbers separately.

3. $\quad 4\frac{2}{5}$ $\qquad 6\frac{3}{10}$ $\qquad 5\frac{4}{11}$ $\qquad 8\frac{7}{13}$

 $\quad + 3\frac{1}{5}$ $\qquad + 8\frac{6}{10}$ $\qquad + 4\frac{5}{11}$ $\qquad + 6\frac{4}{13}$

4. $\quad 3\frac{2}{9}$ $\qquad 6\frac{4}{11}$ $\qquad 7\frac{2}{7}$ $\qquad 9\frac{3}{10}$

 $\quad 5\frac{1}{9}$ $\qquad 9\frac{2}{11}$ $\qquad 8\frac{2}{7}$ $\qquad 2\frac{5}{10}$

 $\quad + 4\frac{5}{9}$ $\qquad + 2\frac{3}{11}$ $\qquad + 5\frac{2}{7}$ $\qquad + 4\frac{1}{10}$

Sometimes the total of an addition problem can be reduced.

EXAMPLE 2 $\dfrac{5}{12} + \dfrac{1}{12} =$

$\qquad$ **STEP 1** Add the numerators. $5 + 1 = 6$

$\qquad$ **STEP 2** Place the total over the denominator. $\dfrac{6}{12}$

$\qquad$ **STEP 3** Reduce the answer. $\dfrac{6 \div 6}{12 \div 6} = \dfrac{1}{2}$

$$\dfrac{5}{12}$$
$$+ \dfrac{1}{12}$$
$$\dfrac{6}{12} = \dfrac{1}{2}$$

....

Add and reduce.

5.
$$\dfrac{5}{8} \qquad \dfrac{4}{9} \qquad \dfrac{3}{12} \qquad \dfrac{7}{15} \qquad \dfrac{3}{16}$$
$$+\dfrac{1}{8} \qquad +\dfrac{2}{9} \qquad +\dfrac{5}{12} \qquad +\dfrac{3}{15} \qquad +\dfrac{5}{16}$$

6.
$$\dfrac{2}{10} \qquad \dfrac{6}{15} \qquad \dfrac{7}{20} \qquad \dfrac{9}{24} \qquad \dfrac{8}{27}$$
$$\dfrac{3}{10} \qquad \dfrac{2}{15} \qquad \dfrac{3}{20} \qquad \dfrac{7}{24} \qquad \dfrac{4}{27}$$
$$+\dfrac{3}{10} \qquad +\dfrac{4}{15} \qquad +\dfrac{4}{20} \qquad +\dfrac{2}{24} \qquad +\dfrac{6}{27}$$

7.
$$5\dfrac{2}{6} \qquad 7\dfrac{5}{12} \qquad 10\dfrac{5}{14} \qquad 13\dfrac{8}{15}$$
$$+6\dfrac{1}{6} \qquad +9\dfrac{3}{12} \qquad +\ 8\dfrac{7}{14} \qquad +29\dfrac{2}{15}$$

8.
$$9\dfrac{2}{9} \qquad 6\dfrac{3}{10} \qquad 10\dfrac{5}{16} \qquad 12\dfrac{3}{8}$$
$$8\dfrac{1}{9} \qquad 7\dfrac{2}{10} \qquad 4\dfrac{3}{16} \qquad 9\dfrac{1}{8}$$
$$+7\dfrac{3}{9} \qquad +4\dfrac{3}{10} \qquad +\ 3\dfrac{4}{16} \qquad +10\dfrac{2}{8}$$

If the total of an addition problem is an improper fraction, change the improper fraction to a mixed number. (See page 19.)

EXAMPLE 3 $\dfrac{5}{8} + \dfrac{7}{8} =$

    STEP 1 Add the fractions. $\dfrac{5}{8} + \dfrac{7}{8} = \dfrac{12}{8}$

    STEP 2 Change $\dfrac{12}{8}$ to a mixed number. $\dfrac{12}{8} = 1\dfrac{4}{8}$

    STEP 3 Reduce $1\dfrac{4}{8}$. $1\dfrac{4 \div 4}{8 \div 4} = 1\dfrac{1}{2}$

$$\dfrac{5}{8} \quad +\dfrac{7}{8}$$
$$\dfrac{12}{8} = 1\dfrac{4}{8} = 1\dfrac{1}{2}$$

    (In the last step, you could reduce $\dfrac{12}{8}$ first. $\dfrac{12}{8} = \dfrac{3}{2} = 1\dfrac{1}{2}$)

....

Add and reduce.

9. $\dfrac{4}{5}$ $\dfrac{6}{8}$ $\dfrac{7}{10}$ $\dfrac{8}{9}$ $\dfrac{3}{6}$

     $+\dfrac{3}{5}$ $+\dfrac{5}{8}$ $+\dfrac{6}{10}$ $+\dfrac{5}{9}$ $+\dfrac{3}{6}$

10. $\dfrac{11}{12}$ $\dfrac{9}{14}$ $\dfrac{7}{8}$ $\dfrac{11}{15}$ $\dfrac{9}{16}$

     $+\dfrac{5}{12}$ $+\dfrac{7}{14}$ $+\dfrac{5}{8}$ $+\dfrac{7}{15}$ $+\dfrac{15}{16}$

11. $\dfrac{5}{9}$ $\dfrac{6}{7}$ $\dfrac{7}{10}$ $\dfrac{9}{12}$ $\dfrac{6}{8}$

     $\dfrac{7}{9}$ $\dfrac{5}{7}$ $\dfrac{3}{10}$ $\dfrac{11}{12}$ $\dfrac{5}{8}$

     $+\dfrac{8}{9}$ $+\dfrac{3}{7}$ $+\dfrac{5}{10}$ $+\dfrac{7}{12}$ $+\dfrac{7}{8}$

12. $8\dfrac{3}{8}$ $9\dfrac{5}{6}$ $5\dfrac{7}{10}$ $2\dfrac{7}{12}$

     $3\dfrac{7}{8}$ $2\dfrac{1}{6}$ $4\dfrac{9}{10}$ $8\dfrac{8}{12}$

     $+5\dfrac{5}{8}$ $+6\dfrac{4}{6}$ $+7\dfrac{5}{10}$ $+6\dfrac{9}{12}$

Adding Fractions with Different Denominators

When the fractions in an addition problem do not have the same denominators, rewrite the problem so that each fraction has the same denominator, called a **common denominator.**

To add a half dollar and a quarter, think of the half dollar as two quarters. As a fraction problem, a half dollar plus a quarter is $\frac{2}{4} + \frac{1}{4} = \frac{3}{4}$ dollar.

A common denominator is a number that can be divided evenly by all the denominators in a problem. The *smallest* number that can be divided evenly by all the denominators in a problem is called the **lowest common denominator** or **LCD.**

Sometimes the largest denominator in a problem is the LCD.

EXAMPLE $\quad \frac{3}{5} + \frac{4}{15} =$

> **STEP 1** Since 5 divides evenly into 15, the LCD is 15.
>
> **STEP 2** Raise $\frac{3}{5}$ to $\frac{9}{15}$. (See page 18.)
>
> **STEP 3** Add the new fractions.

$$\begin{array}{r} \frac{3}{5} = \frac{9}{15} \\[2mm] + \frac{4}{15} = \frac{4}{15} \\ \hline \frac{13}{15} \end{array}$$

Add and reduce.

1.
$\begin{array}{r} \frac{3}{4} \\ + \frac{1}{2} \\ \hline \end{array}$
$\qquad$
$\begin{array}{r} \frac{2}{3} \\ + \frac{5}{6} \\ \hline \end{array}$
$\qquad$
$\begin{array}{r} \frac{7}{8} \\ + \frac{3}{4} \\ \hline \end{array}$
$\qquad$
$\begin{array}{r} \frac{5}{6} \\ + \frac{1}{3} \\ \hline \end{array}$
$\qquad$
$\begin{array}{r} \frac{5}{9} \\ + \frac{2}{3} \\ \hline \end{array}$

2.
$\begin{array}{r} \frac{3}{8} \\ \frac{3}{4} \\ + \frac{1}{2} \\ \hline \end{array}$
$\qquad$
$\begin{array}{r} \frac{1}{6} \\ \frac{5}{12} \\ + \frac{3}{4} \\ \hline \end{array}$
$\qquad$
$\begin{array}{r} \frac{2}{5} \\ \frac{1}{2} \\ + \frac{9}{10} \\ \hline \end{array}$
$\qquad$
$\begin{array}{r} \frac{2}{3} \\ \frac{5}{12} \\ + \frac{1}{4} \\ \hline \end{array}$
$\qquad$
$\begin{array}{r} \frac{3}{5} \\ \frac{1}{3} \\ + \frac{4}{15} \\ \hline \end{array}$

3.
$\begin{array}{r} \frac{3}{4} \\ \frac{1}{2} \\ + \frac{3}{20} \\ \hline \end{array}$
$\qquad$
$\begin{array}{r} \frac{2}{3} \\ \frac{5}{6} \\ + \frac{1}{2} \\ \hline \end{array}$
$\qquad$
$\begin{array}{r} \frac{5}{24} \\ \frac{3}{8} \\ + \frac{1}{3} \\ \hline \end{array}$
$\qquad$
$\begin{array}{r} \frac{4}{9} \\ \frac{5}{6} \\ + \frac{7}{18} \\ \hline \end{array}$
$\qquad$
$\begin{array}{r} \frac{7}{10} \\ \frac{1}{3} \\ + \frac{11}{30} \\ \hline \end{array}$

Finding a Common Denominator

Here are two ways of finding a common denominator when the largest denominator in an addition problem doesn't work.

1. Multiply the denominators together.

2. Go through the multiplication table of the largest denominator.

EXAMPLE 1 $\frac{2}{5} + \frac{3}{4} =$

STEP 1   Multiply the denominators. $5 \times 4 = 20$. 20 is the LCD.

STEP 2   Raise each fraction to 20ths as on page 18.

STEP 3   Add the new fractions.

STEP 4   Change the answer to a mixed number.

$$\frac{2}{5} = \frac{8}{20}$$
$$+\frac{3}{4} = \frac{15}{20}$$
$$\frac{23}{20} = 1\frac{3}{20}$$

EXAMPLE 2 $\frac{2}{3} + \frac{5}{6} + \frac{3}{4} =$

STEP 1   Go through the multiplication table of the 6's.
$6 \times 1 = 6$, which cannot be divided by 4.
$6 \times 2 = 12$, which can be divided by 3 and 4.

STEP 2   Raise each fraction to 12ths.

STEP 3   Add the new fractions.

STEP 4   Change the answer to a mixed number and reduce.

$$\frac{2}{3} = \frac{8}{12}$$
$$\frac{5}{6} = \frac{10}{12}$$
$$+\frac{3}{4} = \frac{9}{12}$$
$$\frac{27}{12} = 2\frac{3}{12} = 2\frac{1}{4}$$

1. $\frac{3}{5}$ $\frac{3}{4}$ $\frac{2}{5}$ $\frac{3}{7}$ $\frac{5}{6}$

    $+\frac{2}{3}$ $+\frac{1}{3}$ $+\frac{1}{2}$ $+\frac{1}{3}$ $+\frac{2}{5}$

2. $\frac{4}{7}$ $\frac{5}{6}$ $\frac{3}{8}$ $\frac{2}{3}$ $\frac{5}{9}$

    $+\frac{3}{4}$ $+\frac{2}{7}$ $+\frac{4}{5}$ $+\frac{4}{11}$ $+\frac{3}{5}$

3.

$$\frac{5}{6}$$
$$+\frac{3}{4}$$

$$\frac{4}{9}$$
$$+\frac{5}{6}$$

$$\frac{7}{10}$$
$$+\frac{3}{4}$$

$$\frac{5}{12}$$
$$+\frac{5}{9}$$

$$\frac{3}{8}$$
$$+\frac{5}{6}$$

4.

$$\frac{2}{3}$$
$$\frac{5}{8}$$
$$+\frac{3}{4}$$

$$\frac{1}{4}$$
$$\frac{3}{5}$$
$$+\frac{7}{10}$$

$$\frac{8}{9}$$
$$\frac{5}{6}$$
$$+\frac{3}{4}$$

$$\frac{5}{16}$$
$$\frac{5}{8}$$
$$+\frac{1}{2}$$

$$\frac{2}{9}$$
$$\frac{1}{2}$$
$$+\frac{5}{6}$$

5.

$$\frac{5}{6}$$
$$\frac{2}{5}$$
$$+\frac{4}{15}$$

$$\frac{7}{12}$$
$$\frac{5}{8}$$
$$+\frac{3}{4}$$

$$\frac{2}{3}$$
$$\frac{1}{6}$$
$$+\frac{11}{12}$$

$$\frac{7}{20}$$
$$\frac{3}{8}$$
$$+\frac{3}{10}$$

$$\frac{4}{9}$$
$$\frac{1}{6}$$
$$+\frac{5}{12}$$

6.

$$\frac{2}{3}$$
$$\frac{4}{9}$$
$$+\frac{5}{6}$$

$$\frac{6}{7}$$
$$\frac{3}{4}$$
$$+\frac{1}{2}$$

$$\frac{2}{9}$$
$$\frac{1}{3}$$
$$+\frac{1}{6}$$

$$\frac{5}{7}$$
$$\frac{4}{9}$$
$$+\frac{2}{3}$$

$$\frac{11}{16}$$
$$\frac{1}{3}$$
$$+\frac{7}{8}$$

Rewrite each problem with whole numbers under whole numbers and fractions under fractions. Then add and reduce.

7. $4\frac{3}{5} + 6\frac{3}{4} =$ $\qquad$ $7\frac{5}{8} + 9\frac{2}{3} =$ $\qquad$ $8\frac{5}{9} + 3\frac{2}{3} =$

8. $6\frac{5}{12} + 7\frac{3}{8} =$ $\qquad$ $10\frac{2}{7} + 8\frac{1}{3} =$ $\qquad$ $6\frac{1}{6} + 4\frac{3}{4} =$

9. $7\frac{9}{10} + 8\frac{1}{4} =$ $3\frac{4}{9} + 12\frac{5}{6} =$ $9\frac{5}{8} + 3\frac{7}{12} =$

10. $8\frac{5}{6} + 2\frac{2}{9} =$ $3\frac{7}{8} + 11\frac{3}{5} =$ $6\frac{9}{10} + 5\frac{2}{3} =$

11. $5\frac{2}{3} + 9\frac{3}{5} + 2\frac{7}{10} =$ $3\frac{3}{8} + 8\frac{1}{6} + 7\frac{3}{4} =$ $2\frac{2}{9} + 10\frac{3}{4} + 4\frac{5}{6} =$

12. $6\frac{1}{2} + 1\frac{1}{3} + 14\frac{1}{4} =$ $7\frac{7}{8} + \frac{2}{3} + 4\frac{1}{2} =$ $9\frac{5}{12} + 11\frac{2}{3} + \frac{4}{9} =$

13. $6\frac{7}{16} + \frac{1}{2} + 8\frac{5}{8} =$ $12\frac{3}{4} + 9\frac{5}{6} + \frac{2}{3} =$ $9\frac{1}{2} + 3\frac{3}{4} + 2\frac{2}{3} =$

14. $\frac{6}{7} + 15\frac{3}{5} + 7\frac{7}{10} =$ $4\frac{5}{12} + \frac{4}{9} + 19\frac{3}{4} =$ $11\frac{7}{8} + 5\frac{3}{7} + \frac{1}{2} =$

Estimating Answers

So far in this book, you have found exact answers. Sometimes an **approximate** answer or an **estimate** is enough. Review "Thinking About the Size of Fractions" on page 14. When you add two fractions, think about the sum. Is the sum equal to one whole (= 1), less than one whole (< 1) or more than one whole (> 1)? Study these examples carefully.

EXAMPLES

$\frac{1}{2} + \frac{1}{2}$, the sum is 1.

$\frac{1}{2}$ + a fraction that is *less* than $\frac{1}{2}$, the sum is *less* than 1.

$\frac{1}{2}$ + a fraction that is *more* than $\frac{1}{2}$, the sum is *more than* 1.

$\frac{1}{2} + \frac{3}{6} = 1$

$\frac{1}{2} + \frac{2}{5} < 1$

$\frac{1}{2} + \frac{4}{5} > 1$

In each box, write <, >, or = to make the statement true.

1. $\frac{5}{16} + \frac{1}{2} \ \square \ 1$ $\frac{4}{8} + \frac{1}{2} \ \square \ 1$ $\frac{1}{2} + \frac{9}{10} \ \square \ 1$ $\frac{3}{6} + \frac{2}{4} \ \square \ 1$

2. $\frac{1}{2} + \frac{3}{8} \ \square \ 1$ $\frac{2}{3} + \frac{5}{6} \ \square \ 1$ $\frac{9}{10} + \frac{2}{3} \ \square \ 1$ $\frac{3}{8} + \frac{4}{9} \ \square \ 1$

In problems 3 through 6, choose the two consecutive numbers that the answer comes between.

3. Is $1\frac{1}{2} + 2\frac{3}{4}$ between 3 and 4 or between 4 and 5?

4. Is $4\frac{1}{8} + 5\frac{1}{3}$ between 9 and 10 or between 10 and 11?

5. Is $3\frac{2}{3} + 7\frac{5}{6}$ between 10 and 11 or between 11 and 12?

6. Is $2\frac{3}{10} + 4\frac{1}{2}$ between 6 and 7 or between 7 and 8?

In problems 7 through 10, write the two consecutive numbers that the answer comes between.

7. $4\frac{7}{8} + 3\frac{9}{10}$ is between _____ and _____.

8. $2\frac{1}{6} + 5\frac{1}{2}$ is between _____ and _____.

9. $5\frac{2}{9} + 1\frac{3}{10}$ is between _____ and _____.

10. $9\frac{1}{2} + 6\frac{5}{7}$ is between _____ and _____.

For more practice, find the exact answers for the problems above.

Applying Your Addition Skills

Addition problems may ask you to combine measurements or to find a total.

Solve and write the correct label, such as inches or miles, next to each answer. Reduce each answer to lowest terms.

1. Karen is $62\frac{1}{2}$ inches tall. Her mother is $5\frac{3}{4}$ inches taller. How tall is Karen's mother?

2. Doing errands on Monday, Mrs. Johnson drove $5\frac{1}{2}$ miles to the supermarket, $3\frac{7}{10}$ miles to the hardware store, $\frac{8}{10}$ mile to the laundry, and $6\frac{1}{10}$ miles back home. What total distance did she drive?

3. Mr. Munro's empty suitcase weighs $4\frac{3}{4}$ pounds. The items he packed in his suitcase weigh $17\frac{3}{5}$ pounds. What was the weight of his suitcase when he filled it?

4. When Petra when shopping, she bought 2 pounds of sugar, $3\frac{1}{4}$ pounds of ground beef, $2\frac{2}{3}$ pounds of cheese, and a $\frac{7}{8}$-pound can of tomatoes. What was the total weight of her purchases?

5. One week John spent his evenings trying to convert his attic into an extra bedroom. Monday night he worked $3\frac{1}{2}$ hours. Tuesday night he worked $4\frac{1}{3}$ hours. Wednesday he worked $2\frac{3}{4}$ hours, and Thursday he worked $3\frac{2}{3}$ hours. How many hours did John work on his attic that week?

6. When Ruby was sick, her weight went down to $116\frac{1}{5}$ pounds. By the time she recovered, she had gained $12\frac{1}{2}$ pounds. What was Ruby's final weight when she was well?

7. Lois talked on the phone for $\frac{1}{2}$ hour this morning, $\frac{3}{5}$ hour in the afternoon, and $1\frac{2}{3}$ hours in the evening. How much time did Lois spend on the phone that day?

Subtracting Fractions with the Same Denominators

The answer to a subtraction problem is called the **difference.** To subtract fractions with the same denominators, subtract the numerators and put the difference over the denominator.

EXAMPLE $\dfrac{5}{12} - \dfrac{1}{12} =$

    STEP 1 Subtract the numerators. $5 - 1 = 4$

    STEP 2 Put the difference, 4, over the denominator. $\dfrac{4}{12}$

    STEP 3 Reduce $\dfrac{4}{12}$ by dividing 4 and 12 by 4.

$$\begin{array}{r} \dfrac{5}{12} \\[6pt] -\dfrac{1}{12} \\ \hline \dfrac{4}{12} = \dfrac{1}{3} \end{array}$$

Subtract and reduce.

1. $\dfrac{5}{9}$ $\dfrac{7}{10}$ $\dfrac{5}{8}$ $\dfrac{4}{13}$ $\dfrac{9}{11}$

     $-\dfrac{2}{9}$ $-\dfrac{6}{10}$ $-\dfrac{1}{8}$ $-\dfrac{1}{13}$ $-\dfrac{3}{11}$

2. $\dfrac{13}{15}$ $\dfrac{15}{16}$ $\dfrac{23}{24}$ $\dfrac{11}{19}$ $\dfrac{17}{20}$

     $-\dfrac{8}{15}$ $-\dfrac{9}{16}$ $-\dfrac{11}{24}$ $-\dfrac{8}{19}$ $-\dfrac{13}{20}$

With mixed numbers, subtract fractions and whole numbers separately.

3. $8\dfrac{6}{7}$ $10\dfrac{5}{8}$ $7\dfrac{8}{9}$ $13\dfrac{9}{10}$

     $-5\dfrac{2}{7}$ $-4\dfrac{5}{8}$ $-6\dfrac{5}{9}$ $-9\dfrac{5}{10}$

4. $15\dfrac{7}{16}$ $14\dfrac{11}{12}$ $18\dfrac{9}{13}$ $23\dfrac{5}{6}$

     $-7\dfrac{3}{16}$ $-5\dfrac{5}{12}$ $-9\dfrac{4}{13}$ $-7\dfrac{1}{6}$

Subtracting Fractions with Different Denominators

If the denominators in a subtraction problem are different, find the LCD and raise the fractions to higher terms. Then follow the rules on page 31.

EXAMPLE $\dfrac{5}{8} - \dfrac{1}{3} =$

STEP 1 The LCD is $8 \times 3 = 24$.

STEP 2 Raise each fraction to 24ths.

STEP 3 Subtract the new fractions.

$$\dfrac{5}{8} = \dfrac{15}{24}$$
$$-\dfrac{1}{3} = \dfrac{8}{24}$$
$$\dfrac{7}{24}$$

Subtract and reduce.

1.
$\dfrac{3}{4}$
$-\dfrac{1}{2}$

$\dfrac{5}{8}$
$-\dfrac{1}{4}$

$\dfrac{5}{6}$
$-\dfrac{1}{3}$

$\dfrac{3}{4}$
$-\dfrac{3}{16}$

$\dfrac{1}{2}$
$-\dfrac{3}{10}$

2.
$\dfrac{2}{3}$
$-\dfrac{1}{4}$

$\dfrac{4}{5}$
$-\dfrac{1}{3}$

$\dfrac{3}{4}$
$-\dfrac{2}{7}$

$\dfrac{5}{6}$
$-\dfrac{3}{5}$

$\dfrac{5}{9}$
$-\dfrac{1}{6}$

3.
$8\dfrac{11}{12}$
$-2\dfrac{3}{8}$

$9\dfrac{5}{7}$
$-3\dfrac{1}{2}$

$12\dfrac{4}{5}$
$-5\dfrac{2}{9}$

$11\dfrac{3}{4}$
$-8\dfrac{7}{10}$

4.
$13\dfrac{4}{7}$
$-7\dfrac{3}{8}$

$21\dfrac{8}{9}$
$-6\dfrac{1}{4}$

$9\dfrac{5}{6}$
$-2\dfrac{2}{5}$

$20\dfrac{9}{11}$
$-8\dfrac{2}{3}$

Rewrite each problem with the first number on top and the second number below it. Then subtract and reduce.

5. $7\frac{1}{2} - 2\frac{1}{4} =$ $12\frac{3}{4} - 9\frac{3}{8} =$ $5\frac{2}{3} - 3\frac{4}{7} =$

6. $4\frac{11}{16} - 2\frac{3}{8} =$ $18\frac{7}{10} - 9\frac{1}{2} =$ $22\frac{8}{15} - 17\frac{2}{9} =$

7. $8\frac{9}{28} - 7\frac{2}{7} =$ $35\frac{11}{30} - 28\frac{1}{3} =$ $14\frac{11}{12} - 7\frac{5}{8} =$

8. $9\frac{11}{36} - 5\frac{2}{9} =$ $15\frac{7}{8} - 8\frac{4}{7} =$ $45\frac{8}{9} - 38\frac{5}{7} =$

9. $5\frac{7}{8} - 4\frac{5}{9} =$ $10\frac{5}{6} - 6\frac{3}{7} =$ $100\frac{5}{8} - 98\frac{1}{6} =$

10. $11\frac{1}{3} - 5\frac{1}{8} =$ $24\frac{5}{6} - 21\frac{4}{5} =$ $8\frac{3}{4} - 6\frac{2}{5} =$

11. $17\frac{3}{4} - 9\frac{2}{3} =$ $15\frac{1}{3} - 7\frac{3}{10} =$ $12\frac{1}{2} - 8\frac{3}{7} =$

12. $13\frac{5}{8} - 11\frac{5}{12} =$ $16\frac{5}{6} - 9\frac{7}{10} =$ $18\frac{3}{5} - 9\frac{3}{10} =$

13. $11\frac{2}{3} - 5\frac{1}{2} =$ $7\frac{1}{2} - 3\frac{2}{5} =$ $19\frac{7}{12} - 8\frac{3}{7} =$

14. $21\frac{14}{15} - 18\frac{7}{10} =$ $13\frac{11}{18} - 8\frac{1}{2} =$ $25\frac{5}{8} - 22\frac{2}{5} =$

Borrowing and Subtracting Fractions

In order to have a fraction to subtract from, you sometimes have to borrow from a whole number. Look at the examples carefully.

EXAMPLE 1 $9 - 6\frac{3}{5} =$

Since there is nothing to subtract the $\frac{3}{5}$ from, you have to borrow.

STEP 1 Borrow 1 from the 9 and change the 1 to 5ths because 5 is the LCD.

$1 = \frac{5}{5}$

$$9 = 8\frac{5}{5}$$
$$-6\frac{3}{5} = 6\frac{3}{5}$$
$$\overline{\phantom{-6\frac{3}{5}} \ \ 2\frac{2}{5}}$$

STEP 2 Subtract the fractions and the whole numbers.

EXAMPLE 2 $12\frac{3}{7} - 8\frac{6}{7} =$

Since you cannot take $\frac{6}{7}$ from $\frac{3}{7}$, you have to borrow.

STEP 1 Borrow 1 from 12 and change the 1 to 7ths because 7 is the LCD.

$1 = \frac{7}{7}$

$$12\frac{3}{7} = 11\frac{7}{7} + \frac{3}{7}$$
$$-\ 8\frac{6}{7}$$
$$\overline{}$$

STEP 2 Add $\frac{7}{7}$ to $\frac{3}{7}$. $\frac{7}{7} + \frac{3}{7} = \frac{10}{7}$

$$11\frac{7}{7} + \frac{3}{7} = 11\frac{10}{7}$$
$$-\ 8\frac{6}{7} = 8\frac{6}{7}$$
$$\overline{ \ 3\frac{4}{7}}$$

STEP 3 Subtract the fractions and the whole numbers.

EXAMPLE 3 $8\frac{1}{3} - 4\frac{3}{4} =$

STEP 1 Raise each fraction to 12ths because 12 is the LCD.

$$8\frac{1}{3} = 8\frac{4}{12}$$
$$-4\frac{3}{4} = 4\frac{9}{12}$$
$$\overline{}$$

STEP 2 Borrow 1 from 8 and change the 1 to 12ths.

$1 = \frac{12}{12}$

$$8\frac{4}{12} = 7\frac{12}{12} + \frac{4}{12}$$
$$-4\frac{9}{12}$$
$$\overline{}$$

STEP 3 Add $\frac{12}{12}$ to $\frac{4}{12}$. $\frac{12}{12} + \frac{4}{12} = \frac{16}{12}$

$$7\frac{12}{12} + \frac{4}{12} = 7\frac{16}{12}$$
$$-4\frac{9}{12} = 4\frac{9}{12}$$
$$\overline{ \ 3\frac{7}{12}}$$

STEP 4 Subtract the fractions and the whole numbers.

Subtract and reduce.

1.　8　　　　4　　　　　12　　　　9　　　　10
$\quad -\dfrac{5}{6}$　　$-\dfrac{3}{7}$　　　$-\dfrac{1}{2}$　　$-\dfrac{2}{5}$　　$-\dfrac{8}{11}$

2.　12　　　　　9　　　　　7　　　　　6　　　　10
$\quad -8\dfrac{3}{7}$　　$-5\dfrac{2}{3}$　　$-5\dfrac{7}{12}$　　$-2\dfrac{5}{9}$　　$-3\dfrac{5}{16}$

3.　$8\dfrac{2}{9}$　　　$11\dfrac{3}{8}$　　　$14\dfrac{7}{12}$　　　$15\dfrac{1}{5}$
$\quad -4\dfrac{5}{9}$　　$-4\dfrac{7}{8}$　　$-6\dfrac{11}{12}$　　$-8\dfrac{4}{5}$

4.　$12\dfrac{7}{15}$　　$22\dfrac{4}{7}$　　　$19\dfrac{1}{3}$　　　$18\dfrac{3}{16}$
$\quad -7\dfrac{8}{15}$　　$-6\dfrac{6}{7}$　　$-12\dfrac{2}{3}$　　$-10\dfrac{7}{16}$

5.　$20\dfrac{1}{8}$　　$36\dfrac{6}{11}$　　　$15\dfrac{7}{20}$　　　$30\dfrac{5}{9}$
$\quad -9\dfrac{5}{8}$　　$-8\dfrac{9}{11}$　　$-14\dfrac{13}{20}$　　$-27\dfrac{8}{9}$

6.　$7\dfrac{1}{3}$　　　$15\dfrac{1}{6}$　　　$10\dfrac{2}{5}$　　　$5\dfrac{2}{3}$
$\quad -4\dfrac{11}{12}$　　$-3\dfrac{2}{3}$　　$-5\dfrac{7}{10}$　　$-2\dfrac{3}{4}$

Rewrite each problem with the first number on top and the second number below it. Then subtract and reduce.

7. $12\frac{2}{5} - 6\frac{3}{4} =$ $14\frac{3}{8} - 9\frac{3}{4} =$ $7\frac{2}{3} - 2\frac{8}{9} =$

8. $18\frac{1}{6} - 3\frac{3}{4} =$ $25\frac{1}{2} - 6\frac{4}{7} =$ $20\frac{5}{12} - 11\frac{5}{6} =$

9. $19\frac{1}{2} - 13\frac{7}{10} =$ $36\frac{4}{9} - 4\frac{3}{5} =$ $17\frac{2}{7} - 8\frac{5}{6} =$

10. $15\frac{3}{8} - 7\frac{4}{5} =$ $30\frac{1}{3} - 16\frac{8}{11} =$ $12\frac{1}{6} - 10\frac{7}{12} =$

11. $14\frac{1}{2} - 13\frac{11}{15} =$ $18\frac{4}{9} - 14\frac{3}{4} =$ $22\frac{5}{8} - 8\frac{6}{7} =$

12. $16\frac{7}{12} - 9\frac{7}{8} =$ $28\frac{1}{6} - 17\frac{3}{5} =$ $15\frac{3}{4} - 8\frac{7}{8} =$

13. $30\frac{1}{4} - 16\frac{5}{12} =$ $19\frac{3}{11} - 18\frac{1}{2} =$ $17\frac{2}{7} - 15\frac{5}{8} =$

14. $35\frac{1}{4} - 18\frac{3}{5} =$ $13\frac{2}{9} - 7\frac{5}{6} =$ $24\frac{3}{16} - 9\frac{2}{3} =$

Applying Your Subtraction Skills

Subtraction problems ask you to figure out what is *left* after you take something away or to find how much something *increases* or *decreases*.

Solve and write the correct label, such as inches or pounds, next to each answer. Reduce each answer to lowest terms.

1. From a board $38\frac{1}{2}$ inches long, Pete cut a piece $17\frac{5}{8}$ inches long. How long was the remaining piece?

2. Jeff weighed 166 pounds. He went on a diet and lost $11\frac{3}{4}$ pounds. How much did Jeff weigh after his diet?

3. Before leaving on a weekend trip, Mr. Green noticed that his mileage gauge registered $20,245\frac{3}{10}$ miles. When he returned home, the gauge registered $20,734\frac{7}{10}$ miles. How many miles did Mr. Green drive that weekend?

4. Adrienne had a piece of cloth 5 yards long. She used $1\frac{2}{3}$ yards to make a new curtain for her bathroom. How long was the remaining piece of cloth?

5. From a 10-foot long pipe, Shirley cut a section $1\frac{11}{12}$ feet long to repair her kitchen drain. How long was the piece of pipe that was left?

6. Tom changed the rotating speed of his cement mixer from $6\frac{1}{3}$ rpm's to 10 rpm's. By how many revolutions per minute did the speed of the mixer increase?

7. From a 100-pound bag of cement, Fred used $44\frac{5}{8}$ pounds to make concrete. How much cement was left in the bag?

8. Esther bought a $\frac{3}{4}$-pound bar of baking chocolate. If she used $\frac{5}{8}$ pound of chocolate to make a cake, how much chocolate was left?

Read each of the following problems carefully to decide whether to add or to subtract.

Mr. Alonso bought 60 feet of nylon rope. To tie a mattress to the roof of his car, he used $18\frac{2}{3}$ feet of the rope. Then to pitch a tent for his son, he used $24\frac{1}{2}$ feet of rope.

9. How much rope did Mr. Alonso use to tie the mattress to the roof of his car and to pitch the tent?

10. After Mr. Alonso used the two pieces of rope, how much rope was left from the original 60 feet?

Mary ran $2\frac{3}{4}$ miles on Monday, $3\frac{3}{8}$ miles on Wednesday, and $1\frac{5}{8}$ miles on Friday.

11. How many miles did Mary run this week?

12. Mary tries to run 10 miles each week. How many more miles does Mary need to run to complete 10 miles?

A town needs $3 million for a new recreation center. So far the town has received $\$\frac{3}{4}$ million from private gifts, $\$1\frac{1}{8}$ million from a state grant, and $\$\frac{1}{2}$ million from a federal grant.

13. What total amount has the town received so far?

14. How much more money does the town need to reach its goal?

An airline allows carry-on bags with a combined length plus width plus height of no more than 37 inches.

15. Selma's bag is $15\frac{3}{4}$ inches long, $9\frac{1}{2}$ inches wide, and $12\frac{7}{8}$ inches high. Does her bag fit within the guidelines for carry-on bags?

16. Bill's bag is $16\frac{1}{2}$ inches long, $8\frac{5}{8}$ inches wide, and $11\frac{3}{8}$ inches high. Does his bag fit within the airline's guidelines for carry-on bags?

Multiplying Fractions

The answer to a multiplication problem is called the **product.** Multiplying fractions means *finding a fraction of a fraction.* When you multiply proper fractions, the product is *smaller* than the fractions you multiply. You are finding a *part of a part.*

To multiply fractions, multiply the numerators together and multiply the denominators together.

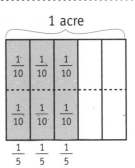

1 acre

EXAMPLE The owner of a $\frac{3}{5}$-acre panel of land plans to sell $\frac{1}{2}$ of the land. How large is the parcel that he plans to sell?

Find $\frac{1}{2}$ of $\frac{3}{5}$.

STEP 1 Multiply the numerators. $1 \times 3 = 3$

STEP 2 Multiply the denominators. $2 \times 5 = 10$

$$\frac{1}{2} \times \frac{3}{5} = \frac{3}{10}$$

ANSWER: The size of the parcel of land is $\frac{3}{10}$ **acre.**

Multiply and reduce.

1. $\frac{2}{3} \times \frac{4}{5} =$ $\frac{5}{7} \times \frac{2}{9} =$ $\frac{1}{8} \times \frac{7}{10} =$ $\frac{3}{11} \times \frac{5}{8} =$

2. $\frac{1}{3} \times \frac{1}{5} =$ $\frac{4}{7} \times \frac{4}{9} =$ $\frac{5}{6} \times \frac{5}{8} =$ $\frac{9}{10} \times \frac{1}{4} =$

3. $\frac{7}{9} \times \frac{2}{5} =$ $\frac{3}{8} \times \frac{7}{8} =$ $\frac{1}{6} \times \frac{5}{6} =$ $\frac{8}{9} \times \frac{2}{9} =$

With three fractions, multiply the numerators of the first two fractions together. Then multiply that answer by the third numerator. Do the same with the denominators.

4. $\frac{3}{5} \times \frac{1}{2} \times \frac{3}{4} =$ $\frac{5}{7} \times \frac{1}{3} \times \frac{1}{2} =$ $\frac{2}{3} \times \frac{1}{3} \times \frac{5}{9} =$

5. $\frac{4}{5} \times \frac{4}{5} \times \frac{1}{3} =$ $\frac{2}{5} \times \frac{7}{9} \times \frac{1}{3} =$ $\frac{1}{3} \times \frac{4}{7} \times \frac{2}{3} =$

Canceling and Multiplying Fractions

Canceling is a shortcut in the multiplication of fractions. It is just like reducing. It means dividing a numerator and a denominator by a number that goes evenly into both before actually multiplying. You don't have to cancel to get the right answer, but it makes the multiplication easier.

EXAMPLE $\dfrac{10}{21} \times \dfrac{14}{25} =$

STEP 1   Cancel 10 and 25 by 5.
10 ÷ 5 = 2 and 25 ÷ 5 = 5.
Cross out the 10 and the 25.

$$\dfrac{\overset{2}{\cancel{10}}}{21} \times \dfrac{14}{\underset{5}{\cancel{25}}} =$$

STEP 2   Cancel 14 and 21 by 7.
14 ÷ 7 = 2 and 21 ÷ 7 = 3.
Cross out the 14 and the 21.

$$\dfrac{\overset{2}{\cancel{10}}}{\underset{3}{\cancel{21}}} \times \dfrac{\overset{2}{\cancel{14}}}{\underset{5}{\cancel{25}}} = \dfrac{4}{15}$$

STEP 3   Multiply across by the new numbers.
2 × 2 = 4 and 3 × 5 = 15

Cancel and multiply.

1. $\dfrac{2}{5} \times \dfrac{3}{4} =$ $\dfrac{4}{9} \times \dfrac{3}{7} =$ $\dfrac{5}{8} \times \dfrac{7}{10} =$ $\dfrac{6}{7} \times \dfrac{5}{12} =$

2. $\dfrac{4}{5} \times \dfrac{1}{6} =$ $\dfrac{8}{15} \times \dfrac{10}{13} =$ $\dfrac{9}{14} \times \dfrac{10}{11} =$ $\dfrac{12}{13} \times \dfrac{1}{15} =$

3. $\dfrac{4}{9} \times \dfrac{3}{8} =$ $\dfrac{5}{12} \times \dfrac{9}{10} =$ $\dfrac{7}{22} \times \dfrac{11}{14} =$ $\dfrac{5}{6} \times \dfrac{9}{10} =$

4. $\dfrac{15}{16} \times \dfrac{12}{25} =$ $\dfrac{7}{24} \times \dfrac{32}{35} =$ $\dfrac{21}{26} \times \dfrac{13}{28} =$ $\dfrac{19}{45} \times \dfrac{25}{38} =$

5. $\dfrac{9}{16} \times \dfrac{8}{15} =$ $\dfrac{6}{7} \times \dfrac{28}{33} =$ $\dfrac{5}{11} \times \dfrac{22}{25} =$ $\dfrac{8}{15} \times \dfrac{9}{32} =$

6. $\dfrac{12}{13} \times \dfrac{3}{16} =$ $\dfrac{4}{9} \times \dfrac{9}{14} =$ $\dfrac{15}{16} \times \dfrac{16}{21} =$ $\dfrac{11}{24} \times \dfrac{8}{11} =$

7. $\dfrac{7}{8} \times \dfrac{9}{14} \times \dfrac{5}{6} =$ $\dfrac{4}{11} \times \dfrac{5}{12} \times \dfrac{11}{15} =$ $\dfrac{16}{21} \times \dfrac{14}{15} \times \dfrac{3}{4} =$

8. $\dfrac{9}{16} \times \dfrac{20}{21} \times \dfrac{7}{10} =$ $\dfrac{4}{15} \times \dfrac{7}{12} \times \dfrac{3}{4} =$ $\dfrac{9}{10} \times \dfrac{1}{6} \times \dfrac{5}{8} =$

9. $\dfrac{7}{24} \times \dfrac{2}{3} \times \dfrac{16}{35} =$ $\dfrac{3}{20} \times \dfrac{18}{25} \times \dfrac{5}{6} =$ $\dfrac{11}{12} \times \dfrac{5}{11} \times \dfrac{8}{15} =$

10. $\dfrac{8}{21} \times \dfrac{1}{3} \times \dfrac{15}{32} =$ $\dfrac{6}{7} \times \dfrac{21}{40} \times \dfrac{4}{15} =$ $\dfrac{19}{36} \times \dfrac{7}{10} \times \dfrac{3}{7} =$

11. $\dfrac{11}{39} \times \dfrac{10}{11} \times \dfrac{13}{18} =$ $\dfrac{17}{21} \times \dfrac{14}{51} \times \dfrac{7}{11} =$ $\dfrac{15}{28} \times \dfrac{7}{16} \times \dfrac{12}{45} =$

Multiplying Fractions and Whole Numbers

Any whole number can be written as a fraction with a denominator of 1. For example, 5 is the same as $\frac{5}{1}$. To check, divide 5 by 1.

EXAMPLE $9 \times \dfrac{5}{6} =$

$$\frac{\overset{3}{\cancel{9}}}{1} \times \frac{5}{\underset{2}{\cancel{6}}} = \frac{15}{2} = 7\frac{1}{2}$$

STEP 1   Write 9 as a fraction. $9 = \dfrac{9}{1}$

STEP 2   Cancel 9 and 6 by 3.

STEP 3   Multiply across by the new numbers.

STEP 4   Change the improper fraction to a mixed number (see page 19).

Multiply and reduce.

1. $4 \times \dfrac{3}{7} =$ 　　　　$9 \times \dfrac{1}{4} =$ 　　　　$\dfrac{2}{3} \times 10 =$ 　　　　$3 \times \dfrac{4}{5} =$

2. $15 \times \dfrac{2}{3} =$ 　　　　$\dfrac{5}{9} \times 18 =$ 　　　　$\dfrac{4}{21} \times 7 =$ 　　　　$\dfrac{8}{15} \times 45 =$

3. $\dfrac{7}{8} \times 24 =$ 　　　　$\dfrac{11}{40} \times 20 =$ 　　　　$32 \times \dfrac{7}{16} =$ 　　　　$12 \times \dfrac{15}{16} =$

4. $35 \times \dfrac{7}{30} =$ 　　　　$16 \times \dfrac{5}{24} =$ 　　　　$\dfrac{7}{12} \times 36 =$ 　　　　$2 \times \dfrac{9}{10} =$

Multiplying Mixed Numbers

To multiply with mixed numbers, change every mixed number to an improper fraction. (See page 21.)

EXAMPLE $4\frac{1}{2} \times \frac{5}{6} =$

$\quad$ **STEP 1** $\,$ Change $4\frac{1}{2}$ to an improper fraction.

$\qquad\qquad 4\frac{1}{2} = \frac{9}{2}$

$\quad$ **STEP 2** $\,$ Cancel 9 and 6 by 3.

$\quad$ **STEP 3** $\,$ Multiply across.

$\quad$ **STEP 4** $\,$ Change the improper fraction to a mixed number (see page 19).

$$\frac{\overset{3}{\cancel{9}}}{2} \times \frac{5}{\underset{2}{\cancel{6}}} = \frac{15}{4} = 3\frac{3}{4}$$

Multiply and reduce.

1. $1\frac{1}{2} \times \frac{1}{4} =$ $\qquad$ $1\frac{2}{3} \times \frac{2}{7} =$ $\qquad$ $2\frac{1}{4} \times \frac{7}{8} =$ $\qquad$ $\frac{3}{10} \times 5\frac{1}{2} =$

2. $\frac{4}{9} \times 3\frac{3}{4} =$ $\qquad$ $\frac{2}{7} \times 2\frac{5}{8} =$ $\qquad$ $4\frac{2}{3} \times \frac{15}{16} =$ $\qquad$ $6\frac{3}{7} \times \frac{4}{5} =$

3. $2\frac{1}{3} \times 1\frac{1}{5} =$ $\qquad$ $6\frac{2}{3} \times 3\frac{3}{4} =$ $\qquad$ $3\frac{5}{7} \times 4\frac{3}{8} =$ $\qquad$ $16\frac{1}{3} \times 2\frac{5}{14} =$

4. $3\frac{3}{4} \times \frac{8}{9} \times 1\frac{1}{5} =$ $\qquad$ $2\frac{2}{5} \times 3\frac{3}{8} \times 2\frac{7}{9} =$ $\qquad$ $2\frac{2}{15} \times 5\frac{1}{4} \times 7\frac{1}{2} =$

Rounding and Estimating

To estimate a multiplication problem with mixed numbers, round each mixed number to the nearest whole number. Then use the whole numbers to multiply.

> For a mixed number with a fraction of $\frac{1}{2}$ or more, round to the next whole number.

EXAMPLES $5\frac{3}{4} \rightarrow 6$ $2\frac{5}{9} \rightarrow 3$ $8\frac{1}{2} \rightarrow 9$

> For a mixed number with a fraction less than $\frac{1}{2}$, drop the fraction and use the whole number.

EXAMPLES $7\frac{3}{8} \rightarrow 7$ $10\frac{1}{3} \rightarrow 10$ $1\frac{2}{7} \rightarrow 1$

EXAMPLE Estimate the answer to $5\frac{3}{4} \times 2$.

STEP 1 Round $5\frac{3}{4}$ to the nearest whole number. $5\frac{3}{4} \rightarrow 6$

STEP 2 Multiply the rounded numbers. $6 \times 2 = 12$

STEP 3 Find the exact answer. Notice how close the estimate, 12, is to the exact answer, $11\frac{1}{2}$.

$$5\frac{3}{4} \times 2 =$$

$$\frac{23}{\cancel{4}_2} \times \frac{\cancel{2}^1}{1} = \frac{23}{2} = \mathbf{11\frac{1}{2}}$$

First round each mixed number to the nearest whole number. Next, find the product of the rounded numbers. Then find the exact answer.

1. $6 \times 2\frac{3}{4} =$ $3\frac{1}{8} \times 4 =$ $5\frac{1}{3} \times 9 =$ $1\frac{5}{6} \times 8 =$

2. $4\frac{3}{5} \times 5 =$ $3 \times 6\frac{2}{9} =$ $12 \times 1\frac{7}{8} =$ $10\frac{1}{4} \times 6 =$

3. $2\frac{2}{9} \times 1\frac{7}{8} =$ $2\frac{2}{7} \times 5\frac{1}{4} =$ $4\frac{2}{3} \times 2\frac{7}{10} =$ $1\frac{1}{5} \times 4\frac{1}{6} =$

4. $2\frac{1}{4} \times 2\frac{2}{3} =$ $3\frac{3}{4} \times 4\frac{4}{9} =$ $5\frac{5}{6} \times 1\frac{13}{20} =$ $3\frac{3}{8} \times 2\frac{5}{9} =$

Applying Your Multiplication Skills

Fraction multiplication problems sometimes ask you to find *a part of* something or to figure out the cost, weight, or size of several things when you have information about only one thing.

Solve and write the correct label, such as hours or pounds, next to each answer. Reduce each answer to lowest terms. Read the problems carefully. Some problems require operations other than multiplication.

1. Jack's regular work week is 40 hours. One week he worked $\frac{4}{5}$ of the time. How many hours did he work that week?

2. From their house to their parents' house, the Leightons have to drive 276 miles. If they have already driven $\frac{2}{3}$ of the distance, how far have they gone?

3. One cubic foot of water weighs $62\frac{1}{2}$ pounds. How much do $3\frac{1}{5}$ cubic feet of water weigh?

4. For a bookcase he is building, Tim wants six shelves each $28\frac{1}{2}$ inches long. What total length of shelving does he need?

5. One yard of lumber costs $2. Use estimation to decide which of the following is closest to the cost of $5\frac{3}{4}$ yards of lumber.

   a. a little under $10
   b. a little under $11
   c. a little under $12

6. Find the exact cost of the lumber in problem 5.

7. Robert works as an apprentice electrician. He makes $15 an hour. Use estimation to decide which of the following is closest to the amount Robert makes for $3\frac{1}{4}$ hours of work.

   a. between $40 and $45
   b. a little over $45
   c. a little over $55

8. Verva drives 18 miles to her current job. A new job that she is considering is $1\frac{1}{2}$ times as far as her current job. What is the driving distance to her new job?

9. A tailor needs $3\frac{1}{6}$ yards of material to make a suit. How much material does he need to make three suits?

10. In the last problem, the tailor made the three suits from a piece of material $12\frac{1}{4}$ yards long. How much material was left?

11. In the weeks before Christmas, Serena worked $11\frac{1}{2}$ hours each day in a department store. For the first 8 hours each day, Serena makes $6.40 an hour. How much did she earn for those 8 hours?

12. For overtime work, Serena gets $1\frac{1}{2}$ times her regular wage. What does she get for one hour of overtime work?

13. How many hours of overtime did Serena work each day?

14. How much does Serena make each day for overtime work?

15. Find Serena's total income for an $11\frac{1}{2}$ hour day.

16. Mary and José want to buy a condominium that costs $88,000. They plan to make a down payment of $\frac{1}{10}$ of the price of the condominium. How much is the down payment?

17. José's parents have offered to give them $5,000 toward the down payment. How much do Mary and José have to take from their savings to complete the down payment?

18. After making the down payment, the remaining cost of Mary and José's condominium is the amount of their mortgage. How much is the mortgage for the condominium?

Dividing Fractions by Fractions

The answer to a division problem is called the **quotient.** The number being divided is the **dividend,** and the number that divides into the dividend is the **divisor.**

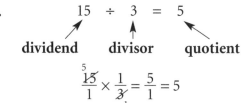

$$15 \div 3 = 5$$

dividend   divisor   quotient

Notice that the whole number division problem, $15 \div 3 = 5$, has the same answer as the fraction multiplication problem, $15 \times \frac{1}{3} = 5$.

$$\frac{\overset{5}{\cancel{15}}}{1} \times \frac{1}{\underset{1}{\cancel{3}}} = \frac{5}{1} = 5$$

The fraction $\frac{1}{3}$ is called the **reciprocal** or the **inverse** of the improper fraction $\frac{3}{1}$. In division problems with fractions, you **invert** the divisor. To invert a fraction, write the denominator on top and the numerator below.

To divide by a fraction, do the following steps:

STEP 1   Invert the fraction to the right of the division sign (the divisor), and change the division sign ($\div$) to a multiplication sign ($\times$).

STEP 2   Follow the rules for multiplication.

EXAMPLE 1   Suppose a gardener wants to divide her $\frac{1}{2}$-acre garden into $\frac{1}{8}$-acre sections. How many $\frac{1}{8}$-acre sections can she make?

To find out how many sections she can make, divide $\frac{1}{2}$ by $\frac{1}{8}$.

1 acre

$\frac{1}{2}$ acre

STEP 1   Invert the divisor $\frac{1}{8}$ to $\frac{8}{1}$ and change the $\div$ sign to $\times$.

STEP 2   Cancel and multiply across.

STEP 3   Change the improper fraction to a whole number. The gardener can make **four** $\frac{1}{8}$-acre sections.

$$\frac{1}{2} \div \frac{1}{8} =$$

$$\frac{1}{\underset{1}{\cancel{2}}} \times \frac{\overset{4}{\cancel{8}}}{1} = \frac{4}{1} = \mathbf{4}$$

ANSWER: 4 sections

EXAMPLE 2 $\frac{3}{4} \div \frac{5}{8} =$

STEP 1   Invert the divisor $\frac{5}{8}$ to $\frac{8}{5}$ and change the $\div$ sign to $\times$.

STEP 2   Cancel and multiply across.

STEP 3   Change the improper fraction to a mixed number.

$$\frac{3}{4} \div \frac{5}{8} =$$

$$\frac{3}{\underset{1}{\cancel{4}}} \times \frac{\overset{2}{\cancel{8}}}{5} = \frac{6}{5} = \mathbf{1\frac{1}{5}}$$

ANSWER: $1\frac{1}{5}$

Divide and reduce.

1. $\dfrac{3}{7} \div \dfrac{2}{5} =$ $\dfrac{4}{9} \div \dfrac{2}{3} =$ $\dfrac{5}{12} \div \dfrac{10}{11} =$ $\dfrac{7}{15} \div \dfrac{4}{5} =$

2. $\dfrac{11}{16} \div \dfrac{5}{8} =$ $\dfrac{8}{9} \div \dfrac{2}{9} =$ $\dfrac{8}{13} \div \dfrac{6}{7} =$ $\dfrac{21}{25} \div \dfrac{7}{10} =$

3. $\dfrac{14}{15} \div \dfrac{16}{27} =$ $\dfrac{35}{36} \div \dfrac{25}{28} =$ $\dfrac{9}{14} \div \dfrac{1}{2} =$ $\dfrac{6}{25} \div \dfrac{1}{5} =$

4. $\dfrac{1}{12} \div \dfrac{7}{9} =$ $\dfrac{4}{11} \div \dfrac{1}{11} =$ $\dfrac{49}{50} \div \dfrac{21}{65} =$ $\dfrac{8}{9} \div \dfrac{5}{12} =$

5. $\dfrac{5}{36} \div \dfrac{11}{42} =$ $\dfrac{13}{63} \div \dfrac{7}{54} =$ $\dfrac{17}{48} \div \dfrac{1}{24} =$ $\dfrac{1}{18} \div \dfrac{8}{27} =$

6. $\dfrac{3}{10} \div \dfrac{6}{7} =$ $\dfrac{5}{11} \div \dfrac{25}{33} =$ $\dfrac{12}{19} \div \dfrac{18}{38} =$ $\dfrac{16}{21} \div \dfrac{3}{4} =$

Dividing Whole Numbers by Fractions

The owner of a 3-acre parcel of land wants to divide the land into $\frac{3}{4}$-acre lots for resale. How many $\frac{3}{4}$-acre lots can be made from the large parcel? To answer this question, you find out how many $\frac{3}{4}$'s there are in 3. In other words, divide 3 by $\frac{3}{4}$.

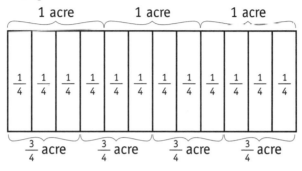

The illustration shows that the owner can make four $\frac{3}{4}$-acre lots.

When dividing a whole number by a fraction, write the whole number as an improper fraction with a denominator of 1.

EXAMPLE 1 $3 \div \frac{3}{4} =$

      STEP 1   Write 3 as the improper fraction $\frac{3}{1}$.

      STEP 2   Invert $\frac{3}{4}$ to $\frac{4}{3}$ and change the ÷ sign to ×.

      STEP 3   Cancel and multiply across.

      STEP 4   Change the improper fraction to a whole number.

$$\frac{3}{1} \div \frac{3}{4} =$$
$$\frac{\overset{1}{\cancel{3}}}{1} \times \frac{4}{\underset{1}{\cancel{3}}} = \frac{4}{1} = 4$$

Notice the answer in the last example. You divided the whole number 3 by a fraction that is smaller than 1. That fraction, $\frac{3}{4}$, divides into 3 *more than* three times.

EXAMPLE 2 $8 \div \frac{6}{7} =$

      STEP 1   Write 8 as the improper fraction $\frac{8}{1}$.

      STEP 2   Invert $\frac{6}{7}$ to $\frac{7}{6}$ and change the ÷ sign to ×.

      STEP 3   Cancel and multiply across.

      STEP 4   Change the improper fraction to a mixed number.

$$\frac{8}{1} \div \frac{6}{7} =$$
$$\frac{\overset{4}{\cancel{8}}}{1} \times \frac{7}{\underset{3}{\cancel{6}}} = \frac{28}{3} = 9\frac{1}{3}$$

Divide and reduce.

1. $12 \div \frac{2}{5} =$ $9 \div \frac{1}{3} =$ $5 \div \frac{3}{4} =$ $6 \div \frac{2}{3} =$

2. $8 \div \frac{3}{8} =$ $25 \div \frac{5}{6} =$ $17 \div \frac{1}{2} =$ $32 \div \frac{8}{9} =$

3. $45 \div \frac{9}{10} =$ $49 \div \frac{7}{12} =$ $36 \div \frac{24}{25} =$ $54 \div \frac{9}{11} =$

4. $48 \div \frac{8}{15} =$ $27 \div \frac{3}{4} =$ $16 \div \frac{3}{5} =$ $30 \div \frac{20}{21} =$

5. $32 \div \frac{4}{21} =$ $45 \div \frac{18}{19} =$ $15 \div \frac{10}{11} =$ $12 \div \frac{9}{10} =$

6. $20 \div \frac{5}{8} =$ $5 \div \frac{15}{16} =$ $7 \div \frac{21}{25} =$ $56 \div \frac{24}{25} =$

Dividing Fractions by Whole Numbers

Think about dividing one more piece of land. If a $\frac{3}{4}$-acre parcel is divided into two equal pieces, what is the size of each parcel? To answer this question, you divide $\frac{3}{4}$ by 2.

1 acre

$\frac{3}{4}$ acre

When dividing a fraction by a whole number, first write the whole number as an improper fraction with a denominator of 1. Then invert that fraction and multiply.

EXAMPLE 1 $\frac{3}{4} \div 2 =$

STEP 1   Write 2 as the improper fraction $\frac{2}{1}$.

STEP 2   Invert $\frac{2}{1}$ to $\frac{1}{2}$ and change the $\div$ sign to $\times$.

STEP 3   Multiply across.

$$\frac{3}{4} \div \frac{2}{1} =$$
$$\frac{3}{4} \times \frac{1}{2} = \frac{3}{8}$$

ANSWER: Each smaller parcel is $\frac{3}{8}$-acre.

In the last example, notice that dividing by 2 is the same as multiplying by $\frac{1}{2}$. In other words, dividing a number by 2 is the same as finding *one-half of the number.*

EXAMPLE 2 $\frac{8}{9} \div 6 =$

STEP 1   Write 6 as the improper fraction $\frac{6}{1}$.

STEP 2   Invert $\frac{6}{1}$ to $\frac{1}{6}$ and change the $\div$ sign to $\times$.

STEP 3   Cancel and multiply across.

$$\frac{8}{9} \div \frac{6}{1} =$$
$$\frac{\overset{4}{\cancel{8}}}{9} \times \frac{1}{\underset{3}{\cancel{6}}} = \frac{4}{27}$$

Divide and reduce.

1. $\frac{4}{5} \div 4 =$　　　$\frac{2}{3} \div 6 =$　　　$\frac{18}{19} \div 9 =$　　　$\frac{1}{4} \div 2 =$

2. $\frac{1}{3} \div 12 =$　　　$\frac{3}{4} \div 7 =$　　　$\frac{5}{6} \div 10 =$　　　$\frac{12}{13} \div 3 =$

3. $\frac{1}{2} \div 11 =$　　　$\frac{3}{5} \div 15 =$　　　$\frac{5}{8} \div 5 =$　　　$\frac{12}{13} \div 18 =$

4. $\frac{20}{21} \div 24 =$　　　$\frac{9}{10} \div 36 =$　　　$\frac{14}{15} \div 35 =$　　　$\frac{24}{25} \div 40 =$

5. $\frac{3}{5} \div 9 =$　　　$\frac{10}{13} \div 30 =$　　　$\frac{12}{17} \div 36 =$　　　$\frac{21}{22} \div 28 =$

6. $\frac{4}{7} \div 44 =$　　　$\frac{15}{16} \div 45 =$　　　$\frac{5}{18} \div 15 =$　　　$\frac{7}{24} \div 35 =$

Dividing with Mixed Numbers

To divide with mixed numbers, first change every mixed number to an improper fraction (see page 21). Also, be sure to write whole numbers as fractions over 1. Then invert the fraction to the right of the division sign and finish the problems as on pages 47, 49, and 51.

EXAMPLE $2\frac{1}{3} \div \frac{1}{4} =$

> **STEP 1**   Write $2\frac{1}{3}$ as the improper fraction $\frac{7}{3}$.
>
> **STEP 2**   Invert $\frac{1}{4}$ to $\frac{4}{1}$ and change the ÷ sign to ×.
>
> **STEP 3**   Since nothing can be canceled, multiply across.
>
> **STEP 4**   Change the improper fraction to a mixed number.

$$\frac{7}{3} \div \frac{1}{4} =$$

$$\frac{7}{3} \times \frac{4}{1} = \frac{28}{3} = 9\frac{1}{3}$$

Divide and reduce.

1. $1\frac{1}{2} \div \frac{3}{4} =$ $1\frac{2}{3} \div \frac{2}{3} =$ $2\frac{3}{4} \div \frac{5}{8} =$ $4\frac{1}{3} \div \frac{2}{9} =$

2. $2\frac{2}{5} \div 6 =$ $3\frac{1}{3} \div 4 =$ $1\frac{5}{7} \div 9 =$ $2\frac{2}{9} \div 15 =$

3. $\frac{5}{8} \div 1\frac{1}{4} =$ $\frac{14}{15} \div 1\frac{1}{6} =$ $\frac{7}{12} \div 2\frac{1}{2} =$ $\frac{9}{16} \div 3\frac{3}{4} =$

4. $12 \div 1\frac{3}{5} =$ $20 \div 2\frac{2}{7} =$ $9 \div 1\frac{7}{8} =$ $24 \div 1\frac{7}{11} =$

5. $3\frac{3}{4} \div 1\frac{1}{8} =$ $\qquad$ $4\frac{1}{2} \div 1\frac{1}{6} =$ $\qquad$ $2\frac{3}{4} \div 1\frac{7}{8} =$ $\qquad$ $1\frac{7}{9} \div 2\frac{2}{9} =$

6. $5\frac{1}{4} \div 4\frac{2}{3} =$ $\qquad$ $6\frac{1}{2} \div 3\frac{1}{4} =$ $\qquad$ $5\frac{3}{5} \div 3\frac{3}{7} =$ $\qquad$ $4\frac{3}{8} \div 1\frac{9}{16} =$

7. $5\frac{2}{3} \div 1\frac{8}{9} =$ $\qquad$ $4\frac{2}{5} \div 8\frac{4}{5} =$ $\qquad$ $3\frac{5}{9} \div 1\frac{13}{15} =$ $\qquad$ $10\frac{2}{3} \div 2\frac{2}{3} =$

8. $3\frac{3}{5} \div 1\frac{7}{20} =$ $\qquad$ $6\frac{3}{5} \div 2\frac{1}{5} =$ $\qquad$ $3\frac{3}{7} \div 1\frac{11}{21} =$ $\qquad$ $2\frac{4}{13} \div 2\frac{1}{4} =$

9. $4\frac{1}{3} \div 2\frac{1}{7} =$ $\qquad$ $6\frac{7}{8} \div 5\frac{1}{4} =$ $\qquad$ $9\frac{7}{10} \div 1\frac{4}{5} =$ $\qquad$ $8\frac{2}{3} \div 5\frac{1}{12} =$

10. $7\frac{1}{2} \div 3\frac{1}{5} =$ $\qquad$ $3\frac{5}{9} \div 2\frac{5}{18} =$ $\qquad$ $5\frac{5}{6} \div 3\frac{5}{12} =$ $\qquad$ $10\frac{5}{8} \div 4\frac{1}{2} =$

Finding a Number When a Fraction of It Is Given

There is a kind of division problem that is sometimes hard to recognize. Think about the question: $\frac{1}{2}$ of what number is 12? Without using pencil and paper, you can probably come up with the answer 24. You know that $\frac{1}{2}$ of 24 is 12.

To solve the problem, you find a solution to the statement $\frac{1}{2} \times ? = 12$. The statement asks you to find the missing number in a multiplication problem. Division is the opposite operation of multiplication. To find the missing number, divide 12 by $\frac{1}{2}$.

You will learn more about opposite operations when you study algebra.

EXAMPLE $\frac{1}{2}$ of what number is 12?

STEP 1   Write 12 as the improper fraction $\frac{12}{1}$. $\frac{12}{1} \div \frac{1}{2} =$

STEP 2   Invert $\frac{1}{2}$ to $\frac{2}{1}$ and change the $\div$ sign to $\times$. $\frac{12}{1} \times \frac{2}{1} = \frac{24}{1} = \mathbf{24}$

STEP 3   Multiply across.

STEP 4   Change the improper fraction to a whole number.

Solve.

1. $\frac{1}{3}$ of what number is 5? $\frac{1}{4}$ of what number is 22?

2. $\frac{2}{3}$ of what number is 18? $\frac{5}{6}$ of what number is 60?

3. $\frac{3}{4}$ of what number is 15? $\frac{5}{8}$ of what number is 40?

4. $\frac{2}{5}$ of what number is 30? $\frac{7}{12}$ of what number is 14?

5. $\frac{3}{8}$ of what number is 36? $\frac{1}{6}$ of what number is 11?

6. $\frac{4}{5}$ of what number is 80? $\frac{8}{9}$ of what number is 32?

7. $\frac{3}{10}$ of what number is 45? $\frac{7}{12}$ of what number is 35?

Applying Your Division Skills

Word problems with division of fractions are tricky because you need to invert the correct number. Remember that the amount being *divided, cut,* or *shared* must be written to the *left* of the ÷ sign. For example, if $5\frac{1}{2}$ pounds of peanuts are to be divided equally among three people, write $5\frac{1}{2}$ first. The problem becomes $5\frac{1}{2} \div 3$. The number on the *right* gets inverted.

Solve and write the correct label, such as pounds or inches, next to each answer. Reduce each answer to lowest terms. Read each problem carefully. Some problems require operations other than division.

1. How many pieces of wood each $7\frac{1}{2}$ inches long can be cut from a board that is 45 inches long?

2. Sandy baked $4\frac{1}{2}$ pounds of cookies. She divided the cookies equally among two friends and herself. How many pounds of cookies did each person get?

3. A tailor needs $3\frac{2}{3}$ yards of material to make a suit. How many suits can she make from 22 yards of material?

4. How many $1\frac{1}{2}$-pound loaves of bread can be made from 9 pounds of dough?

5. How many $\frac{3}{4}$-pound cans of tomatoes can be filled with 24 pounds of tomatoes?

6. To make picture frames, Carlos plans to cut a piece of wooden molding 75 inches long into small strips each $8\frac{1}{3}$ inches long. Assuming there is no waste, how many strips can he cut from the long piece?

7. Sarah needs $2\frac{1}{4}$ yards of material to make a dress for her daughter. How many dresses can she make from $10\frac{1}{2}$ yards of material?

8. On a quiz Adriano got $\frac{7}{8}$ of the problems correct. He had 21 problems correct. How many problems were on the test?

9. Jenny has paid $\frac{1}{4}$ of her car loan. So far she has paid $900. What was the total amount of the loan?

10. In the last problem, how much does Jenny still owe on her car loan?

11. On a snowy evening only $\frac{2}{3}$ of the registered students in Bob's chess class came to school. Eighteen students attended that night. How many students are registered in Bob's class?

12. In the last problem, how many of the registered students were absent on the snowy evening?

13. Workers in a factory were asked if they thought safety conditions were adequate. Ninety of the workers answered that they thought conditions were satisfactory. They represent $\frac{3}{5}$ of all the workers who were questioned. How many workers were questioned?

14. In the last problem, how many of the workers did not think that safety conditions were adequate?

15. On the first day of the fishing season, Jed caught $10\frac{1}{2}$ pounds of trout. He decided to keep half of the amount for himself. How many pounds of trout did he keep?

16. In the last problem, Jed gave the remaining trout to three friends. If they each got the same weight, how much trout did each receive?

17. The budget of $$1\frac{1}{2}$ million to renovate a school gym will be shared equally between the state and the local community. How much does the local community have to pay for the renovation?

18. In the last problem, the school expects to get $\frac{1}{3}$ of the amount that the community owes for the gym renovation from donations. The rest will come from taxes. How much will the community have to raise in taxes?

Fractions Review

This review covers the material you have studied so far in this book. When you finish, check your answers at the back of the book.

1. A yard contains 36 inches. 21 inches is what fraction of a yard?

2. Which fractions in this list are less than $\frac{1}{2}$? $\quad \frac{3}{6}, \frac{7}{15}, \frac{4}{9}, \frac{5}{8}$

3. Reduce $\frac{18}{32}$ to lowest terms.

4. Write $\frac{50}{12}$ as a mixed number.

5. Write $11\frac{5}{8}$ as an improper fraction.

6. Change $\frac{3}{4}$ to twelfths.

7. $9\frac{7}{8} + 6\frac{5}{8} + 3\frac{3}{8} =$

8. $4\frac{3}{5} + 8\frac{1}{2} + 7\frac{2}{3} =$

9. Without finding the exact sum, tell whether $\frac{5}{8} + \frac{5}{9}$ is less than 1, greater than 1, or equal to 1.

10. Mr. Gutierrez usually takes $\frac{3}{4}$ hour to drive home from work. Because of a traffic jam, he took an extra $1\frac{2}{3}$ hours to get home one night. How long did that ride take him?

11. Find the combined weight of three packages that weigh $5\frac{1}{2}$ pounds, $4\frac{7}{16}$ pounds, and $3\frac{3}{8}$ pounds.

12. $10\frac{7}{8} - 5\frac{2}{5} =$

13. $15\frac{2}{11} - 9\frac{7}{11} =$

14. $13\frac{2}{9} - 4\frac{5}{6} =$

15. From a 2-pound box of chocolates, Rachel ate $1\frac{1}{4}$ pounds. What was the weight of the remaining chocolates?

16. The distance from Ellen's home to her school is $4\frac{1}{3}$ miles. If she has already traveled $2\frac{1}{2}$ miles, how far does she have to go?

17. $\dfrac{5}{9} \times \dfrac{4}{7} =$

18. $\dfrac{6}{7} \times \dfrac{14}{15} \times \dfrac{1}{2} =$

19. $2\dfrac{1}{7} \times 1\dfrac{5}{9} =$

20. In the problem $2\dfrac{4}{5} \times 6\dfrac{1}{4}$, round each number to the nearest whole number. Then multiply.

21. What is the total weight of four cartons if each carton weighs $16\dfrac{1}{4}$ pounds?

22. If 1 foot of wire costs 18¢, how much do $5\dfrac{1}{3}$ feet of wire cost?

23. $\dfrac{8}{15} \div \dfrac{7}{12} =$

24. $14 \div \dfrac{4}{9} =$

25. $\dfrac{6}{13} \div 12 =$

26. $3\dfrac{1}{8} \div 5\dfrac{5}{6} =$

27. $\dfrac{4}{5}$ of what number is 60?

28. A carpenter needs $3\dfrac{1}{2}$ yards of lumber to build a bookcase. How many bookcases can he build from 21 yards of lumber?

29. For a $7\dfrac{1}{2}$ hour day, Ed makes $90. How much does he make in 1 hour?

Fractions Review Chart

If you missed more than one problem on any group below, review the practice pages for those problems. Then redo the problems you got wrong before going on to the Decimal Skills Inventory. If you had a passing score, redo any problem you missed and begin the Decimal Skills Inventory on page 60.

PROBLEM NUMBERS	SKILL AREA	PRACTICE PAGES
1, 2, 3, 4, 5, 6	understanding fractions	11–21
7, 8, 9, 10, 11	adding fractions	22–30
12, 13, 14, 15, 16	subtracting fractions	31–38
17, 18, 19, 20, 21, 22	multiplying fractions	39–46
23, 24, 25, 26, 27, 28, 29	dividing fractions	47–57

DECIMALS

Decimal Skills Inventory

This inventory will tell you whether you need to work through the decimals section of this book. Do all the problems that you can. Work carefully and check your answers, but do not use outside help. Correct answers are listed by page number at the back of the book.

1. Write seventy-six thousandths as a decimal.

2. Write 3.04 as a mixed number and reduce.

3. Write $\frac{5}{12}$ as a decimal.   4. Which is larger, 0.076 or 0.08?

5. Rewrite the following list in order from smallest to largest:
   0.087, 0.7, 0.08, 0.07

6. Round 2.093 to the nearest tenth.

7. $4.3 + 0.079 + 0.06 =$ 8. $21 + 2.86 + 0.093 =$

9. Find the total weight of three packages that weigh 2.3 pounds, 4.15 pounds, and 5.65 pounds.

10. At 5:00 on a June morning, the temperature was 62.4°. By 2:00 in the afternoon, the temperature had risen 21.7°. What was the temperature at 2:00 that afternoon?

11. $9.6 - 0.457 =$ 12. $12 - 0.37 =$

13. From a piece of yarn 3 yards long, Sylvia cut a piece 1.85 yards long. How long was the remaining piece?

14. When Fred began driving Saturday morning, his mileage gauge read 8249.6 miles. When he returned home that night, it read 8536.4 miles. How far did Fred drive that day?

15. $2.07 \times 5.3 =$ **16.** $0.038 \times 0.6 =$ **17.** $4.92 \times 10 =$

18. Diane drove her car at an average speed of 45 miles per hour for 3.2 hours. How far did she drive in that time?

19. At $8.60 an hour, how much does a worker make in 7.25 hours?

20. $12.04 \div 14 =$ **21.** $23.36 \div 3.2 =$ **22.** $5.55 \div 0.015 =$

23. $15 \div 0.075 =$ **24.** $49.6 \div 100 =$

25. If 1.4 pounds of beef cost $3.64, how much does 1 pound of beef cost?

26. One yard contains 0.914 meter. How many yards are there in 4.57 meters?

Decimals Inventory Chart

If you missed more than one problem on any group below, work through the practice pages for that group. Then redo the problems you got wrong on the Decimals Inventory Test. If you had a passing score on all five groups of problems, redo any problem that you missed and begin the Percent Skills Inventory on page 96.

PROBLEM NUMBERS	SKILL AREA	PRACTICE PAGES
1, 2, 3, 4, 5, 6	understanding decimals	62–72
7, 8, 9, 10	adding decimals	73–74
11, 12, 13, 14	subtracting decimals	75–78
15, 16, 17, 18, 19	multiplying decimals	79–85
20, 21, 22, 23, 24, 25, 26	dividing decimals	86–93

Understanding Decimals

A decimal is a type of fraction that you work with every day. The following numbers have decimal fractions: $3.75, $64.08, and $1.20. Each number represents dollars and cents. The point in each number separates whole dollar amounts from fractions of a dollar.

There are 100 cents in a dollar. One cent is *one hundredth* of a dollar. The number $3.75 represents three whole dollars and $\frac{75}{100}$ of a dollar. Digits to the left of the decimal point are in whole number places. Digits to the right are in decimal places.

Our money system has just two decimal places. They are dimes or tenths of a dollar and pennies or hundredths of a dollar. Study the chart below. It tells the names of seven whole number places and six decimal places.

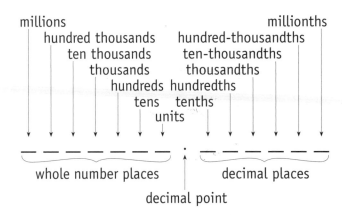

Notice how similar the names are on each side of the decimal point. The first place to the left of the units (or ones) is *tens*. The first place to the right of the units is *tenths*. The third place to the left of units is *thousands*. The third place to the right of units is *thousandths*.

The *-ths* at the end of each decimal place name means that the value of a digit in these places is a fraction of one unit or one whole.

EXAMPLE 1 In the decimal 0.135, which digit is in the *thousandths* place?

Thousandths are the third place to the right of the decimal point. In 0.135 the digit 5 is in the thousandths place.

EXAMPLE 2 What is the value of the digit 3 in the decimal 0.135?

Since 3 is in the second decimal place, it has a value of 3 hundredths.

A number with digits on both sides of the decimal point is sometimes called a **mixed decimal.**

<u>EXAMPLE 3</u> In the number 19.64, which digits are in the decimal places?

The digits 6 and 4 are in the decimal places.

....

For each number, underline the digit that is in the place named.

1. the *tenths* place

    1.3   0.5864   297.18   43.682

2. the *dimes* (or *tenths*) place

    $0.43 $107.21 $6.39 $80.10

3. the *hundredths* place

    0.56   2.974   0.1389   63.4528

4. the *pennies* (or *hundredths*) place

    $3.59 $10.67 $1.026 $295.43

5. the *thousandths* place

    1.234   0.18956   0.04107   0.00385

6. the *ten-thousandths* place

    15.46935   0.02684   3.14159   0.00067

Circle the correct answer for each question.

7. Which of the following tells the value of the digit 9 in the number 2.936?

    9 tenths   9 hundredths   9 thousandths   9 ten-thousandths

8. Which of the following tells the value of the digit 7 in the number 12.047?

    7 tenths   7 hundredths   7 thousandths   7 ten-thousandths

Reading Decimals

To read a decimal, first read it as though it were a whole number. Then give it a decimal name according to the number of decimal places. Remember that the number of places to the right of the decimal point tells you the decimal name. Use the chart on page 62 as a reminder. In the following examples, notice how zeros hold places. With mixed decimals, watch for the word *and* which separates whole numbers from decimal fractions.

EXAMPLES

Decimal	Number of Decimal Places	Words
0.06	two	*six hundredths*
0.0042	four	*forty-two ten-thousandths*
7.003	three	*seven and three thousandths*
19.5	one	*nineteen and five tenths*

For problems 1 through 6, fill in the blanks with the correct decimal name.

1. 0.8 = eight _____   0.3 = three _____   0.06 = six _____

2. 0.17 = seventeen _____   0.09 = nine _____   0.005 = five _____

3. 0.023 = twenty-three _____   0.0028 = twenty-eight _____

4. 0.308 = three hundred eight _____   0.0006 = six _____

5. 4.02 = four and two _____   20.012 = twenty and twelve _____

6. 90.3 = ninety and three _____   5.0041 = five and forty-one _____

For problems 7 through 11, write each decimal or mixed decimal in words.

7. 0.5 =   2.9 =

8. 0.07 =   3.12 =

9. 0.016 =   1.003 =

10. 0.009 =   7.021 =

11. 0.0016 =   10.402 =

Writing Decimals

To write decimals from words, be sure that you have the correct number of decimal places. Use zeros to hold places where necessary. Remember, again, that the word *and* separates whole numbers from decimal fractions in mixed decimals. Study the following examples carefully. Watch where zeros hold places.

EXAMPLES

Words	Number of Decimal Places	Decimal
eight hundredths	two	0.08
thirty-six thousandths	three	0.036
fifty-one millionths	six	0.000051
two and five thousandths	three	2.005
twelve and nine tenths	one	12.9

Write the following as a decimal or a mixed decimal.

1. seven tenths   four and nine tenths

2. sixty-three hundredths   twenty-two thousandths

3. two hundredths   eighty-five hundredths

4. four tenths   nineteen thousandths

5. twelve and three tenths   forty-one hundredths

6. one and five hundredths   two hundred six thousandths

7. forty-eight and nine tenths   eight thousandths

8. three hundred four thousandths   eleven and seven hundredths

9. fifteen ten-thousandths   four and thirteen thousandths

10. two hundred thirty and one tenth   seventy-one ten-thousandths

11. forty-seven thousandths   eight and two ten-thousandths

12. five hundred-thousandths   nineteen millionths

Getting Rid of Unnecessary Zeros

Think about the zeros in the number 020.060 and decide whether each zero is necessary. The number is *twenty and six hundredths* or *twenty and sixty thousandths*.

The zero *left* of the digit 2 is unnecessary.
The zero *right* of 2 is necessary because it keeps the 2 in the tens place.
The zero *left* of 6 is necessary because it keeps 6 in the hundredths place.
The zero *right* of 6 is unnecessary.

The number can be correctly rewritten as 20.06.

> **Note:** The sentence above ends with a period. Do not confuse the period at the end of a sentence with a decimal point.

A decimal with no whole number is often written with a zero in the units place. The decimals .8 and 0.8 are both correct forms for *eight tenths*.

For each number, choose the correctly rewritten number.

1. 5.0060

   a. 50.6   **b.** 50.06   **c.** 5.006   **d.** 5.06

2. 003.1050

   a. 3.105   **b.** 30.105   **c.** 3.15   **d.** 30.015

3. 0700.40

   a. 70.04   **b.** 70.4   **c.** 700.04   **d.** 700.4

4. 0040.0920

   a. 40.92   **b.** 40.092   **c.** 4.092   **d.** 4.92

5. 00.1060

   a. .106   **b.** 0.106   **c.** 0.16   **d.** both a and b

6. 0.03400

   a. 0.34   **b.** 0.034   **c.** .34   **d.** both b and c

Changing Decimals to Fractions

To change a decimal to a fraction (or to change a mixed decimal to a mixed number), write the digits in the decimal as the numerator. Write the denominator according to the number of decimal places. Then reduce the fraction.

EXAMPLE 1 Write 0.24 as a common fraction.

> **STEP 1** Write 24 as the numerator. Since two places means hundredths, write 100 as the denominator.
>
> **STEP 2** Reduce by dividing 24 and 100 by 4.

$$\frac{24 \div 4}{100 \div 4} = \frac{6}{25}$$

EXAMPLE 2 Write 9.015 as a mixed number.

> **STEP 1** Write 9 as the whole number and 15 as the numerator. Since three places means thousandths, write 1,000 as the denominator.
>
> **STEP 2** Reduce by dividing 15 and 1,000 by 5.

$$9\frac{15 \div 5}{1000 \div 5} = 9\frac{3}{200}$$

Write each number as a common fraction or a mixed number and reduce.

1. $0.08 =$ $0.375 =$ $0.0048 =$

2. $3.6 =$ $9.86 =$ $10.002 =$

3. $0.085 =$ $5.08 =$ $0.0025 =$

4. $7.2 =$ $0.15 =$ $8.16 =$

5. $0.00324 =$ $19.0786 =$ $123.462 =$

6. $16.00004 =$ $7.22 =$ $3.000008 =$

7. $2,036.8 =$ $48.02 =$ $3.075 =$

Changing Fractions to Decimals

Remember that a fraction can be understood as a division problem. To change a fraction to a decimal, divide the denominator into the numerator. To divide, add a decimal point and zeros to the numerator. Usually two zeros are enough. Then bring the point up in the answer.

EXAMPLE 1 Write $\frac{1}{2}$ as a decimal.

  STEP 1   Divide 2 into 1. Add a decimal point and a zero to 1.

  STEP 2   Divide and bring up the decimal point.

$$\overset{0.5}{2\overline{)1.0}}$$

EXAMPLE 2 Write $\frac{3}{20}$ as a decimal.

  STEP 1   Divide 20 into 3. Add a decimal point and two zeros to 3.

  STEP 2   Divide and bring up the decimal point.

$$\overset{0.15}{20\overline{)3.00}}$$

EXAMPLE 3 Write $\frac{2}{3}$ as a decimal.

  STEP 1   Divide 3 into 2. Add a decimal point and two zeros to 2.

  STEP 2   Divide and bring up the decimal point.

$$\overset{0.66\frac{2}{3}}{3\overline{)2.00}}$$

In the last example, the division will not come out evenly no matter how many zeros you add. After two places, write the remainder as a fraction over the number you divided by.

Write each fraction as a decimal.

1. $\frac{1}{4} =$ $\frac{2}{5} =$ $\frac{5}{8} =$ $\frac{1}{3} =$

2. $\frac{2}{9} =$ $\frac{6}{25} =$ $\frac{1}{6} =$ $\frac{3}{8} =$

3. $\frac{5}{6} =$ $\frac{3}{10} =$ $\frac{4}{7} =$ $\frac{5}{12} =$

4. $\frac{3}{5} =$ $\frac{9}{10} =$ $\frac{1}{12} =$ $\frac{4}{9} =$

5. $\frac{2}{15} =$ $\frac{3}{4} =$ $\frac{1}{8} =$ $\frac{12}{25} =$

Using a Calculator to Change Fractions to Decimals

A calculator is a useful tool for getting quick, exact answers. Remember that a fraction can be understood as a division problem. To use a calculator to change a fraction to a decimal, divide the numerator by the denominator.

EXAMPLE 1 Use a calculator to change $\frac{3}{4}$ to a decimal.

Press the following keys on a calculator: [3] [÷] [4] [=]

The calculator display should read ⌊   0.75⌋

Notice that the calculator shows a zero in the units place. With fractions that do not divide evenly, a calculator shows repeating digits.

EXAMPLE 2 Use a calculator to change $\frac{2}{3}$ to a decimal.

Press the following keys on a calculator: [2] [÷] [3] [=]

The calculator display should read ⌊   0.6666666⌋

EXAMPLE 3 Use a calculator to change $\frac{5}{4}$ to a mixed decimal.

Press the following keys on a calculator: [5] [÷] [4] [=]

The calculator display should read ⌊   1.25⌋

Use a calculator to change each of the following to a decimal or a mixed decimal.

1. $\frac{4}{5} =$ $\frac{1}{6} =$ $\frac{5}{12} =$ $\frac{9}{10} =$

2. $\frac{3}{8} =$ $\frac{2}{9} =$ $\frac{5}{16} =$ $\frac{1}{3} =$

3. $\frac{7}{25} =$ $\frac{1}{5} =$ $\frac{7}{8} =$ $\frac{3}{10} =$

4. $\frac{5}{2} =$ $\frac{8}{5} =$ $\frac{4}{3} =$ $\frac{7}{4} =$

5. $\frac{11}{6} =$ $\frac{13}{10} =$ $\frac{9}{8} =$ $\frac{13}{2} =$

Comparing Decimals

When you look at a group of decimal fractions, it is sometimes difficult to tell which decimal is the largest. To compare decimals, give each decimal the same number of places by adding zeros. This is the same as giving each decimal fraction a common denominator. The zeros you add do not change the value of the decimals.

EXAMPLE 1 Which is larger, 0.07 or 0.2?

| STEP 1 | Add a zero to 0.2 so that both decimals have two places. | 0.07 or 0.20 |

| STEP 2 | Since twenty hundredths is larger than seven hundredths, 0.2 is larger. | **0.2 is larger** |

EXAMPLE 2 Arrange the following list of decimals in order from smallest to largest: 0.8, 0.08, 0.088, 0.808

| STEP 1 | Add zeros so that each decimal has the same number of places. | 0.800, 0.080, 0.088, 0.808 |

| STEP 2 | Compare and arrange the decimals in order from smallest to largest. | **0.08, 0.088, 0.8, 0.808** |

Notice that the extra zeros are not written in the final list.

In each pair, tell which decimal is larger.

1. 0.04 or 0.008   0.9 or 0.99   0.67 or 0.707

2. 0.328 or 0.33   0.0792 or 0.11   0.2 or 0.099

3. 0.0057 or 0.006   0.4 or 0.0444   0.065 or 0.07

Arrange each list in order from the smallest to the largest.

4. 0.03, 0.33, 0.033, 0.303   0.082, 0.28, 0.8, 0.08

5. 0.106, 0.16, 0.061, 0.6   0.017, 0.2, 0.02, 0.007

6. 0.4, 0.405, 0.45, 0.045   0.04, 0.304, 0.32, 0.4

7. 0.0072, 0.07, 0.027, 0.02   0.2, 0.06, 0.0602, 0.026

Rounding Decimals

To estimate answers to whole number problems, you can first round the numbers to numbers that end with zero. For example, to estimate the answer to 42×68, first round each number to the nearest ten. Then multiply the rounded numbers. $40 \times 70 = 2800$

Rounding is also a useful skill for estimating answers to decimal problems.

To round a decimal, do the following steps.

STEP 1 Underline the digit in the place you are rounding to.

STEP 2 **a.** If the digit to the right of the underlined digit is *greater than or equal to 5,* add 1 to the underlined digit.

b. If the digit to the right of the underlined digit is *less than 5,* leave the underlined digit as is.

STEP 3 Drop all the digits to the right of the underlined digit.

EXAMPLE 1 Round 2.38 to the nearest tenth.

STEP 1 Underline 3, the digit in the tenths place. $2.\underline{3}8 \rightarrow$ **2.4**

STEP 2 The digit to the right of 3 is 8. Since 8 is greater than 5, add 1 to 3. $3 + 1 = 4$

STEP 3 Drop the digit to the right of 4.

EXAMPLE 2 Round 0.1627 to the nearest hundredth.

STEP 1 Underline 6, the digit in the hundredths place. $0.1\underline{6}27 \rightarrow$ **0.16**

STEP 2 The digit to the right of 6 is 2. Since 2 is less than 5, leave 6 as is.

STEP 3 Drop the digits to the right of 6.

When you round a decimal and add 1 to the digit 9, *two* decimal places will change. Study the next example carefully.

EXAMPLE 3 Round 3.00964 to the nearest thousandth.

STEP 1 Underline 9, the digit in the thousandths place $3.00\underline{9}64 \rightarrow$ **3.010**

STEP 2 The digit to the right of 9 is 6. Since 6 is greater than 5, add 1 to 9. $9 + 1 = 10$. Write 0 in the thousandths place and 1 in the hundredths place.

STEP 3 Drop the digits to the right of the thousandths place.

Notice that the rounded number 3.010 ends in zero. You learned on page 66 that the zero to the right of 1 is unnecessary. However, the instruction in the example was to round the number to the nearest thousandth. The number 3.010 expresses thousandths.

....

Round each decimal to the nearest place value given.

1. tenth   4.29   0.638   516.24   27.053

2. hundredth   0.582   12.487   0.0946   2.095

3. thousandth   23.4861   0.0537   5.4068   0.00349

4. whole number (units or ones)   17.26   1.89   356.541   199.8

5. dollar (units or ones) $14.39 $9.78 $1.66 $347.09

6. dime (tenth) $2.79 $63.52 $0.98 $5.34

7. penny (hundredth) $0.987 $4.675 $23.954 $1.085

Round 49.07583 to the nearest place value given.

8. tenth   hundredth   thousandth   ten-thousandth   unit

Use a calculator to write each fraction as a decimal. Then round the calculator answer to the nearest _hundredth_.

9. $\frac{5}{8} =$ $\frac{2}{3} =$ $\frac{3}{7} =$ $\frac{7}{9} =$

Use a calculator to write each fraction as a decimal. Then round the calculator answer to the nearest _thousandth_.

10. $\frac{1}{12} =$ $\frac{5}{6} =$ $\frac{3}{16} =$ $\frac{2}{15} =$

Adding Decimals

To add decimals, first line them up with *point under point*. Remember that any whole number is understood to have a decimal point at its right.

EXAMPLE $2.46 + 0.005 + 16 =$

STEP 1   Line up *point under point*. Notice the decimal point   2.46
         after the whole number 16.   0.005
                                                                     $\underline{+\ 16.}$
STEP 2   Add.   **18.465**

Add.

1. $0.8 + 0.047 + 0.36 =$ $4.9 + 17 + 3.28 =$

2. $123 + 2.6 + 9.04 =$ $32.637 + 5 + 1.98 =$

3. $9.043 + 0.27 + 15 =$ $8.04 + 26 + 31.263 =$

4. $0.849 + 1.6 + 73 =$ $0.0097 + 2.8 + 16 =$

5. $7.563 + 0.08 + 124.9 =$ $83.007 + 0.47 + 9.8 =$

6. $12.3 + 0.908 + 6 + 4.25 =$ $0.0073 + 0.0196 + 0.08 + 0.4 =$

7. $1.6 + 23 + 12.73 + 0.485 =$ $0.09 + 2.6 + 18 + 1.445 =$

Applying Your Addition Skills

Solve and write the correct label, such as inches or pounds, next to each answer.

1. The average monthly rainfall in New York City is 2.96 inches in June, 3.69 inches in July, and 4.01 inches in August. What is the total rainfall for these three months?

2. Thursday Jack drove 278.5 miles. Friday he drove 243.7 miles. Saturday he drove 386 miles, and Sunday he drove 291.8 miles. What total distance did he drive those four days?

3. Aldo welded together pieces of pipe that were 25.6 inches long, 19.8 inches long, and 31.5 inches long. How long was the pipe made of the three welded pieces?

4. Dorothy bought 2.6 pounds of beef, 1.75 pounds of cheese, 3 pounds of chicken, and 2.35 pounds of fish. What was the total weight she had to carry?

5. The distance from Middletown to Springfield is 72.6 miles. The distance from Springfield to Centerville is 48.9 miles. What is the distance from Middletown to Centerville by driving through Springfield?

6. Maceo's normal temperature is 98.6°. When he had a fever, his temperature went up 4.5°. What was his temperature when he had a fever?

7. Find the total weight of three cartons that weigh 4.2 kilograms, 2.37 kilograms, and 0.45 kilogram.

8. In a recent year, the population of Mexico was 94.3 million people. Experts think that in 2025 the population of Mexico will be 35.9 million more people. If the experts are correct, what will be the population of Mexico in 2025?

Subtracting Decimals

To subtract decimals, put the larger number on top and line up the decimal points. Use zeros to give each decimal the same number of decimal places. Then subtract and bring down the decimal point.

EXAMPLE $15.2 - 0.184 =$

STEP 1   Put 15.2 on top and line up the decimal points.

STEP 2   Write two zeros to the right of 15.2 to give 15.2 the same number of decimal places as 0.184.

STEP 3   Subtract and bring down the decimal point.

$$\begin{array}{r} 15.200 \\ -\ 0.184 \\ \hline \mathbf{15.016} \end{array}$$

Subtract.

1. $4.2 - 3.76 =$ $0.804 - 0.1673 =$ $3.2 - 2.68 =$

2. $0.2 - 0.078 =$ $60.4 - 6.04 =$ $89.3 - 0.766 =$

3. $12 - 0.936 =$ $1 - 0.047 =$ $13 - 0.932 =$

4. $8.4 - 0.631 =$ $0.07 - 0.002 =$ $5 - 2.493 =$

5. $96 - 7.485 =$ $3.2 - 0.1986 =$ $0.47 - 0.3992 =$

6. $1.3 - 1.064 =$ $0.81 - 0.793 =$ $2 - 0.807 =$

7. $0.08 - 0.0156 =$ $1.4 - 0.978 =$ $0.6 - 0.059 =$

Rounding and Estimating

Rounding is a useful way to estimate answers to decimal problems.

EXAMPLE   For the problem $0.625 - 0.18$, round each number to the nearest *tenth*. Then subtract the rounded numbers.

STEP 1   Round each number to the nearest tenth. $0.625 - 0.18 \approx 0.6 - 0.2$
The symbol $\approx$ means "is approximately equal to."

STEP 2   Subtract the rounded numbers. $0.6 - 0.2 = \textbf{0.4}$

A calculator is a good tool for checking decimal answers. To get the exact answer for the last example, do the following:

Press the following keys on a calculator: $\cdot$ 6 2 5 $-$ $\cdot$ 1 8 $=$

The calculator display should read   0.445

Round each number to the indicated place. Then add or subtract the rounded numbers. Use a calculator to find the exact answer to each problem.

For problems 1 through 3, first round each number to the nearest *tenth*.

1. $1.41 + 0.865 + 2.74 =$ $26.23 - 8.593 =$

2. $0.59 + 0.127 + 0.08 =$ $0.738 - 0.49 =$

3. $2.88 + 10.319 + 6.0895 =$ $7.286 - 0.51 =$

For problems 4 and 5, first round each number to the nearest *unit* or *whole number*.

4. $16.3 + 2.908 + 136.1 =$ $42.71 - 11.085 =$

5. $11.28 + 4.91 + 3.047 =$ $5.283 - 1.679 =$

For problem 6, first round each number to the nearest *hundredth*.

6. $0.253 + 1.087 + 0.562 =$ $0.928 - 0.3746 =$

Applying Your Subtraction Skills

Subtraction problems ask you to figure out what is *left* after something is taken away or they ask you to compare quantities. Remember to put the larger number on top.

Solve and write the correct label, such as years or meters, next to each answer.

1. In one state the average man lives for 72.6 years. The average woman lives for 79 years. In that state the average woman's life expectancy is how much more than the average man's life expectancy?

2. The area of Philadelphia is 135.1 square miles. The area of Pittsburgh is 55.6 square miles. The area of Philadelphia is how much greater than the area of Pittsburgh?

3. From a board that was 2 meters long, Colin cut off a piece 1.67 meters long. How long was the piece that was left?

4. The distance from Smiths' house to the cabin where they plan to spend their vacation is 91.4 miles on the interstate highway and 104.2 miles on more scenic back roads. The scenic road is how much longer than the interstate highway?

5. When Sam began driving Monday morning his mileage gauge read 16,428.7 miles. When he stopped driving Monday night, it read 16,831.4 miles. How many miles did Sam drive that day?

6. The metal platform of a bridge is 124.2 meters long in the summer. In the winter it shrinks by 1.05 meters. How long is the bridge platform in the winter?

7. One year there were 57.2 million cable television subscribers in the U.S. The next year there were 63 million subscribers. By how many did the number of subscribers increase?

8. The price of 1 pound of beef rose from $3.79 to $4.16. By how much did the price of 1 pound of beef increase?

Read the next problems carefully to decide whether you should add or subtract.

9. Andy works in the shipping department of a publisher. He has to send a buyer three textbooks that weigh 0.8 kilogram, 0.44 kilogram, and 0.65 kilogram. What is the total weight of the three books?

10. On the carton that Andy plans to use for shipping the books, there is a label that says the carton can hold a maximum of 2 kilograms. How much over or under the maximum is the total weight of the three books?

11. One summer the average price of a gallon of gasoline in Cleveland was $1.094 while the average price of gasoline in New York City was $1.332. To the nearest penny, how much more did a gallon of gasoline cost in New York City than in Cleveland?

12. At the same time as the problem above, the average price of a gallon of gasoline in Honolulu was $1.569. To the nearest penny, how much more was the price of a gallon of gasoline in Honolulu than in Cleveland?

13. According to the U.S. Census Bureau, there were a total of 93.3 million households in the U.S. in 1990. The projection for 2010 is that there will be 114.8 million households in the U.S. By how many is the number of households expected to increase from 1990 to 2010?

14. The normal September rainfall for Denver is 1.24 inches. The normal rainfall for Miami in September is 7.63 inches. To the nearest tenth of an inch, how much more rain does Miami get than Denver?

15. Miami gets the least rain in January when the normal rainfall is 2.01 inches. Use the information in the last problem to tell how much more rain Miami gets in September than it gets in January.

16. A nationally read newspaper sells 1.6 million copies each day. Of these copies, 0.4 million are distributed by train, and 0.15 million are distributed by plane. The rest are distributed by truck. How many copies of the newspaper are distributed by truck each day?

Multiplying Decimals

To multiply decimals, multiply the two numbers the same way you would whole numbers. Then count the number of decimal places in both numbers you are multiplying. Decimal places are to the right of the decimal point. Put the total number of places in your answer.

EXAMPLE 1 $4.36 \times 2 =$

two decimal places	4.36
no decimal places	$\times$ 2
two decimal places	**8.72**

Multiply.

1.

3.8	0.92	6.7	5.3	0.84
$\times$ 4	$\times$ 9	$\times$ 6	$\times$ 8	$\times$ 7

2.

41	78	59	86	19
$\times 0.03$	$\times 0.5$	$\times 0.09$	$\times 0.4$	$\times 0.06$

3.

34.7	2.89	0.551	60.3	7.18
$\times$ 8	$\times$ 7	$\times$ 6	$\times$ 9	$\times$ 4

4.

906	504	783	652	467
$\times 0.07$	$\times 0.002$	$\times 0.8$	$\times 0.06$	$\times 0.003$

5.

2.85	0.693	44.7	8.01	9.17
$\times$ 50	$\times$ 40	$\times$ 30	$\times$ 70	$\times$ 60

You may need to add zeros in front of your answer to have enough decimal places in the final answer.

EXAMPLE 2 $0.06 \times 0.4 =$

two decimal places	0.06
one decimal place	$\times$ 0.4
needs one zero to make three places	_24
three decimal places	**0.024**

....

6.

0.09	0.05	0.004	0.08	0.002
$\times$ 0.6	$\times$ 0.7	$\times$ 0.3	$\times$ 0.04	$\times$ 0.8

7.

5.6	0.73	9.2	0.087	3.3
$\times$ 0.2	$\times$ 0.08	$\times$ 0.7	$\times$ 0.4	$\times$ 0.06

8.

41.8	3.90	0.516	73.8	3.47
$\times$ 0.7	$\times$ 0.08	$\times$ 0.5	$\times$ 0.06	$\times$ 0.4

9.

4.5	0.48	0.92	3.4	0.39
$\times$ 2.6	$\times$ 5.2	$\times$ 8.9	$\times$ 0.71	$\times$ 0.56

10.

0.27	5.6	4.9	0.83	9.2
$\times$ 1.8	$\times$ 0.39	$\times$ 5.4	$\times$ 0.17	$\times$ 0.66

Rewrite each problem and multiply.

11. $2.8 \times 4.3 =$ $5.6 \times 0.82 =$ $0.72 \times 5.7 =$

Note: Parentheses with no operation signs between them also mean to multiply.

---

12. $(0.81)(0.69) =$ $(0.94)(1.8) =$ $(30.5)(0.27) =$

13. $7.4 \times 6.6 =$ $61.8 \times 4.8 =$ $0.514 \times 0.91 =$

14. $(9.06)(7.3) =$ $(45.21)(5.6) =$ $(3.748)(73) =$

15. $206.9 \times 0.28 =$ $0.7488 \times 4.9 =$ $34.7 \times 209 =$

16. $(6.82)(5.31) =$ $(0.925)(78.8) =$ $(8.43)(0.409) =$

17. $17.32 \times 0.16 =$ $0.0648 \times 2.3 =$ $913.2 \times 0.049 =$

18. $(40.21)(20.8) =$ $(0.2789)(0.17) =$ $(3.845)(29.2) =$

19. $5{,}183.6 \times 0.0016 =$ $303.003 \times 56.8 =$ $7.05 \times 0.408 =$

Multiplying Decimals by 10, 100, and 1,000

To multiply a decimal by 10, move the decimal point *one place to the right.*

<u>EXAMPLE 1</u> $0.26 \times 10 =$

Move the decimal point one place to the right.
$0.26 \times 10 = 2.6 = \textbf{2.6}$

To multiply a decimal by 100, move the decimal point *two places to the right.* You may have to add zeros to get enough places.

<u>EXAMPLE 2</u> $3.7 \times 100 =$

Move the decimal point two places to the right.
$3.7 \times 100 = 3\,70 = \textbf{370}$

To multiply a decimal by 1,000, move the decimal point *three places to the right.*

<u>EXAMPLE 3</u> $1.4 \times 1,000 =$

Move the decimal point three places to the right.
$1.4 \times 1,000 = 1\,400 = \textbf{1,400}$

Multiply.

1. $0.8 \times 10 =$	$0.09 \times 10 =$	$3.64 \times 10 =$	$0.721 \times 10 =$
2. $0.03 \times 100 =$	$0.275 \times 100 =$	$8.9 \times 100 =$	$0.863 \times 100 =$
3. $0.9 \times 1,000 =$	$2.36 \times 1,000 =$	$0.475 \times 1,000 =$	$1.6 \times 1,000 =$
4. $0.34 \times 10 =$	$1.24 \times 100 =$	$3.85 \times 1,000 =$	$0.06 \times 1,000 =$
5. $\$1.25 \times 10 =$	$\$0.60 \times 100 =$	$\$2.25 \times 1,000 =$	$\$0.03 \times 1,000 =$

Rounding and Estimating

To estimate an answer to a decimal multiplication problem, round each number to the *left-most* place that does not have a zero. Then multiply the rounded numbers. This is sometimes called **front-end rounding.**

EXAMPLE   Use front-end rounding to estimate the answer to 2.84×0.72.

STEP 1   Round 2.84 to the nearest unit, and round 0.72 to $2.84 \times 0.72 \approx 3 \times 0.7$
the nearest tenth.

STEP 2   Multiply the rounded numbers. $3 \times 0.7 = \textbf{2.1}$

To get the exact answer for the last example, press the following keys on a calculator:

| 2 | · | 8 | 4 | × | · | 7 | 2 | = |

The calculator display should read   2.0448

In a decimal multiplication problem, leave any single, non-zero digit as is. For example, to use front-end rounding to estimate the answer to 4.7×0.3, round 4.7 to the nearest unit and leave 0.3 as is.

Use front-end rounding to estimate an answer to each problem. Then use a calculator to find the exact answer.

1. $4.7 \times 0.3 =$ $0.83 \times 0.09 =$ $6.4 \times 0.8 =$

2. $7.9 \times 0.06 =$ $0.58 \times 0.3 =$ $1.82 \times 0.7 =$

3. $5.2 \times 3.7 =$ $0.62 \times 4.1 =$ $0.74 \times 0.53 =$

4. $0.74 \times 0.38 =$ $9.1 \times 0.67 =$ $0.81 \times 0.44 =$

5. $1.907 \times 5.2 =$ $42.7 \times 0.41 =$ $0.681 \times 9.2 =$

Applying Your Multiplication Skills

In each problem pay close attention to the language that tells you to multiply. In most cases you will be given information about one thing, and you will be asked to find information for several things.

Solve and write the correct label, such as kilometers or pounds, next to each answer.

1. One inch is equal to 2.54 centimeters. A 12-inch ruler is how many centimeters long? Round your answer to the nearest tenth.

2. Alberto earns $9.80 an hour. If he worked 7.5 hours on Monday, how much did he earn that day?

3. One mile is equal to 1.6 kilometers. Miriam drives 25 miles to get to her job. What is the distance to her job in kilometers?

4. An airplane flew at an average speed of 386 miles per hour for 2.75 hours. How far did the airplane fly?

5. One pound is equal to 0.45 kilogram. Find the weight in kilograms of a person who weighs 160 pounds.

6. One cubic foot of water weighs 62.5 pounds. What is the weight of 16 cubic feet of water?

7. Jane earns $14.90 for an hour of overtime work. How much does she earn for 2.3 hours of overtime work?

8. At $13.40 a meter, how much do 4.25 meters of material cost?

9. One yard is equal to 0.914 meter. The lot where the Johnson family plans to build a house is 75 yards long. To the nearest meter (unit), what is length of the lot?

10. It costs $0.84 per hour to run the lights in a small theater. How much does it cost to run the lights for 4.5 hours?

Read the next problems carefully to decide which operation to use.

11. What is the cost of 0.85 pound of cheese at $5.90 per pound? Round your answer to the nearest cent.

12. In the last problem, how much change should a customer who bought the cheese receive from a $10 bill?

13. Mike pays a commercial rate for electricity at his TV repair shop. One month Mike used 883 kilowatt-hours of electricity at the rate of $0.153 per kilowatt hour. What was the cost for his electrical use? Round your answer to the nearest cent.

14. Mike had to pay a monthly fee of $7.82 and tax of $8.11 to the electric company. What was his total bill for electricity that month?

15. The average household in Middleville has 2.3 people. There are approximately 15,000 households in Middleville. Use the number of people per household to estimate the population of the town.

16. The gasoline tank in Deborah's car holds 13.2 gallons. When her gas gauge says that the tank is $\frac{1}{4}$ full, how many gallons of gasoline does the tank have?

17. In the last problem, when Deborah's gasoline tank is $\frac{1}{4}$ full, how many gallons must she add to fill the tank?

18. On Carmen's last phone bill, she had 23 minutes of calls at $0.129 per minute and 64 minutes of calls at $0.14 per minute. What was the total charge for these calls? Round your answer to the nearest cent.

19. On Carmen's phone bill, she also had to pay a monthly service charge of $10.75. What was her phone bill?

Dividing Decimals by Whole Numbers.

To divide a decimal by a whole number, bring the decimal point up in the answer directly above its position in the problem. Then divide as you would whole numbers.

<u>EXAMPLE 1</u> $9.32 \div 4 =$

$$\begin{array}{r} 2.33 \\ 4\overline{)9.32} \end{array}$$

Remember that there are several ways to write a division problem. In each example below, 9.32 is the **dividend,** 4 is the **divisor,** and 2.33 is the answer or the **quotient.**

$$\begin{array}{r} 2.33 \\ 4\overline{)9.32} \end{array} \qquad 9.32 \div 4 = 2.33 \qquad \frac{9.32}{4} = 2.33 \qquad 9.32/4 = 2.33$$

You may have to put a zero in the quotient as a decimal placeholder.

<u>EXAMPLE 2</u> $0.222 \div 6 =$

    STEP 1 Bring the decimal point up in the quotient and put a zero in the tenths place.

$$\begin{array}{r} .037 \\ 6\overline{)0.222} \end{array}$$

    STEP 2 Divide.

Divide.

1. $6\overline{)13.8}$ $9\overline{)70.2}$ $4\overline{)0.384}$ $7\overline{)57.75}$

2. $8\overline{)0.192}$ $3\overline{)148.8}$ $5\overline{)19.45}$ $4\overline{)2.524}$

Rewrite each problem and divide.

3. $76.8 \div 16 =$ $7.56 \div 21 =$ $1.52 \div 19 =$ $216.6 \div 38 =$

4. $\dfrac{9.516}{52} =$ $\dfrac{1,565.2}{43} =$ $\dfrac{464.31}{77} =$ $\dfrac{33.605}{65} =$

Dividing Decimals by Decimals

To divide a decimal by a decimal, first change the problem to a new problem with a whole number divisor. Then move the point in the dividend the same number of places that you moved the point in the divisor. Study the example carefully.

EXAMPLE $4.374 \div 0.03 =$

STEP 1 Move the decimal point in the divisor to the right as far as it will go.

$$0.03\overline{)4.374}$$

STEP 2 Move the decimal point in the dividend the same number of places that you moved the decimal point in the divisor.

$$0.03\overline{)4.37\,4}$$

STEP 3 Bring the decimal point up above its new position and divide.

$$\begin{array}{r} 145.8 \\ 0.03\overline{)4.37\,4} \end{array}$$

When you move the decimal point in both the divisor and the dividend, you get a new problem that has the same answer. This is easier to understand with whole numbers.

Think about the problem $12 \div 4 = 3$. If you multiply both the divisor and the dividend by 10, you get the problem $120 \div 40 = 3$, which has the same answer.

Divide.

1. $0.8\overline{)7.68}$ $0.7\overline{)26.6}$ $0.6\overline{)0.42}$ $0.4\overline{)2.76}$

2. $4.1\overline{)1.148}$ $9.2\overline{)128.8}$ $5.3\overline{)4.399}$ $3.2\overline{)0.288}$

Rewrite each problem and divide.

3. $0.882 \div 0.06 =$ $0.5404 \div 0.28 =$ $453.75 \div 0.75 =$ $6.656 \div 0.52 =$

4. $1.17 \div 0.9 =$ $0.888 \div 3.7 =$ $5.92 \div 0.16 =$ $1.334 \div 0.46 =$

Sometimes you need to add zeros in a problem in order to have enough places to move the decimal point.

EXAMPLE 2 $4.8 \div 0.08 =$

STEP 1 Move the decimal point in the divisor two places to the right.

$$0.08\overline{)4.8}$$

STEP 2 To move the decimal point two places to the right in the dividend, add one zero.

$$0.08\overline{)4.80}$$

STEP 3 Bring the decimal point up and divide.

$$0.08\overline{)4.80} \quad \mathbf{60.}$$

....

Divide.

5. $0.007\overline{)5.32}$ $\quad$ $0.009\overline{)4.32}$ $\quad$ $0.003\overline{)8.1}$ $\quad$ $0.008\overline{)77.12}$

6. $0.016\overline{)212.8}$ $\quad$ $0.025\overline{)0.1}$ $\quad$ $0.091\overline{)65.52}$ $\quad$ $0.68\overline{)57.8}$

Rewrite each problem and divide.

7. $0.78 \div 0.0024 =$ $\quad$ $42.84 \div 0.0006 =$ $\quad$ $1.683 \div 0.0018 =$ $\quad$ $15.184 \div 0.0073 =$

8. $\dfrac{156.8}{0.32} =$ $\quad$ $\dfrac{1{,}381.5}{0.45} =$ $\quad$ $\dfrac{4.48}{0.008} =$ $\quad$ $\dfrac{558.6}{0.06} =$

9. $\dfrac{0.522}{8.7} =$ $\quad$ $\dfrac{0.3933}{0.19} =$ $\quad$ $\dfrac{145.44}{3.6} =$ $\quad$ $\dfrac{0.11648}{0.64} =$

Dividing Whole Numbers by Decimals

To divide a whole number by a decimal, put a decimal point after the whole number and add zeros in order to move the decimal point enough places. Remember that a whole number is understood to have a decimal point at its right.

EXAMPLE $35 \div 0.007 =$

STEP 1 Move the decimal point in the divisor three places to the right.	$0.007 \overline{)35}$
STEP 2 Put a decimal point to the right of the whole number. Then write three zeros and move the decimal point three places to the right.	$0.007 \overline{)35.000}$
STEP 3 Bring the decimal point up and divide.	$\begin{array}{r} 5\,000. \\ 0.007 \overline{)35.000} \end{array}$

Divide.

1. $0.4 \overline{)28}$ $0.9 \overline{)360}$ $0.03 \overline{)111}$ $0.08 \overline{)512}$

2. $0.007 \overline{)63}$ $0.0005 \overline{)4}$ $0.06 \overline{)234}$ $0.3 \overline{)1{,}884}$

Rewrite each problem and divide.

3. $\dfrac{18}{0.09} =$ $\dfrac{12}{0.003} =$ $\dfrac{40}{0.02} =$ $\dfrac{7}{0.25} =$

4. $\dfrac{552}{1.2} =$ $\dfrac{2{,}592}{0.36} =$ $\dfrac{2{,}135}{4.27} =$ $\dfrac{21{,}546}{51.3} =$

5. $\dfrac{1{,}178}{0.019} =$ $\dfrac{37{,}440}{0.48} =$ $\dfrac{33{,}040}{5.6} =$ $\dfrac{3{,}237}{0.039} =$

Dividing Decimals by 10, 100, and 1,000

To divide a decimal by 10, move the decimal point *one place to the left*.

EXAMPLE 1 $7.2 \div 10 =$

Move the decimal point one place to the left.

$7.2 \div 10 = 7\,2 = \textbf{0.72}$

To divide a decimal by 100, move the decimal point *two places to the left*. You may have to add zeros to get enough places.

EXAMPLE 2 $3.64 \div 100 =$

Move the decimal point two places to the left.

$3.64 \div 100 = 03\,64 = \textbf{0.0364}$

To divide a decimal by 1,000, move the decimal point *three places to the left*.

EXAMPLE 3 $25.3 \div 1,000 =$

Move the decimal point three places to the left.

$25.3 \div 1,000 = 025\,3 = \textbf{0.0253}$

Divide.

1. $0.9 \div 10 =$	$36 \div 10 =$	$27.3 \div 10 =$	$0.04 \div 10 =$
2. $14.2 \div 100 =$	$1.3 \div 100 =$	$728 \div 100 =$	$0.6 \div 100 =$
3. $37.5 \div 1,000 =$	$1.8 \div 1,000 =$	$2 \div 1,000 =$	$428 \div 1,000 =$
4. $13.45 \div 10 =$	$0.32 \div 100 =$	$6,954 \div 1,000 =$	$15.8 \div 1,000 =$
5. $\$2.90 \div 10 =$	$\$650 \div 100 =$	$\$540 \div 1,000 =$	$\$20 \div 1,000 =$

Dividing to Fixed Place Accuracy

Adding zeros to a division of decimals problem does not always result in a problem that divides evenly. To get a division answer that is accurate to the nearest *tenth,* divide to the hundredths place and round the answer to the nearest tenth. This is called dividing to **fixed place accuracy.** In this case, the fixed place is tenths.

EXAMPLE   Find the answer to $4.3 \div 0.7$ to the nearest tenth.

STEP 1   Move the decimal point in both the divisor and the dividend one place to the right.

$$0.7\overline{)4.3}$$

STEP 2   Add two zeros to get one more place beyond the tenths place.

$$0.7\overline{)4.3\,00}$$

STEP 3   Divide to the hundredths place and round the answer to the nearest tenth.

$$\begin{array}{r} 6.14 \to \mathbf{6.1} \\ 0.7\overline{)4.3\,00} \end{array}$$

To check the example on a calculator, press the following keys:

| 4 | · | 3 | ÷ | · | 7 | = |

The calculator display should read 6.1428571 , which to the nearest tenth is **6.1.**

Find the answer to each problem to the nearest tenth. Use a calculator to check your answers.

1. $2 \div 1.8 =$ $4.1 \div 0.36 =$ $0.4 \div 0.12 =$

2. $1.2 \div 9 =$ $0.17 \div 0.6 =$ $5 \div 0.7 =$

3. $37.4 \div 12 =$ $0.45 \div 2.1 =$ $18 \div 0.13 =$

4. $49.5 \div 36 =$ $10.3 \div 0.35 =$ $204 \div 9.2 =$

5. $12.3 \div 7 =$ $72.6 \div 50.3 =$ $63 \div 0.8 =$

Applying Your Division Skills

In each problem pay close attention to the language that tells you to divide.

A problem may give information about several things and ask you to find information for one of these things.

You may be asked to find an average which is a total divided by the number of items that make up the total.

Or, you may be asked to calculate a **rate.** A rate is an amount whose unit of measure contains a word such as *per* or *for each*. A slash (/) often indicates rate, for example miles/gallon for miles per gallon.

Solve and write the correct label, such as pounds or miles, next to each answer.

1. Together, the four members of the Rosa family weigh 508.8 pounds. What is the average weight of one member of the family?

2. Mark drove a total of 1,247.5 miles in 5 days. What was the average number of miles he drove each day?

3. The cost of 3.5 yards of material is $33.60. Find the cost of 1 yard of the material.

4. Margie made $477.40 last week. She makes $12.40 an hour. How many hours did she work last week?

5. If a plane flew 2,419.2 miles in 6.3 hours, what was its average speed in miles per hour?

6. If 2.3 pounds of vegetables cost $3.68, what is the price of 1 pound of vegetables?

7. There are 1.6 kilometers in a mile. How many miles are there in 36.8 kilometers?

8. There are 2.54 centimeters in 1 inch. How many inches are there in 45.72 centimeters?

9. In baseball, a batting average is the number of hits a player gets divided by the number of times he is at bat. Batting averages are measured in *thousandths*. Find the batting average of a player who gets 17 hits in 52 times at bat. (**Hint:** Divide to the ten-thousandths place and round your answer to the nearest thousandth.)

10. Find the batting average of another baseball player who got 14 hits in 45 times at bat.

11. In basketball, a scoring average is the number of points a player gets divided by the number of games he plays. Basketball scoring averages are measured in *tenths*. One season Michael Jordan scored 2,431 points in 82 games. Find his scoring average for the season. (**Hint:** Divide to the hundredths place and round your answer to the nearest tenth.)

12. Find the scoring average of another basketball player who scored 1,710 points in 80 games.

13. Sandra drove 475 miles on 22 gallons of gasoline. To the nearest tenth, how many miles per gallon did she get?

14. In one week a factory produced 700 chairs. There are 18 workers in the factory. To the nearest whole number, how many chairs were produced per worker that week?

15. A post office handled 1,500 pieces of out-going mail in 9 hours. To the nearest whole number, how many pieces of mail were handled per hour?

Cumulative Review

This review covers the material you have studied so far in this book. When you finish, check your answers at the back of the book.

1. $3\frac{1}{8} + 5\frac{2}{3} =$

2. $10\frac{1}{2} - 6\frac{5}{9} =$

3. $5\frac{1}{3} \times 2\frac{1}{4} =$

4. $2\frac{1}{2} \div \frac{5}{8} =$

5. Write fourteen ten-thousandths as a decimal.

6. Write 0.016 as a fraction and reduce.

7. Write $\frac{7}{16}$ as a decimal.

8. Which is larger, 0.0013 or 0.02?

9. Rewrite the following list in order from smallest to largest:
0.03, 0.031, 0.1, 0.013

10. What is 12.384 rounded to the nearest tenth?

11. $0.056 + 2.3 + 19 =$

12. $8 + 1.0573 + 1.64 =$

13. Janet bought 2.6 pounds of beef, 1.3 pounds of cheese, 2.45 pounds of chicken, and 5 pounds of sugar. What was the total weight she had to carry?

14. $12.3 - 0.097 =$

15. $3 - 0.654 =$

16. In polishing a piece of pipe that was 2 inches thick, 0.016 inch of metal was worn away. What was the thickness of the pipe when it was polished?

17. $63.2 \times 0.045 =$

18. $20.8 \times 100 =$

19. In the problem 91.12 × 7.8, round 91.12 to the nearest *ten* and 7.8 to the nearest *unit*. Then multiply.

20. One inch is equal to 2.54 centimeters. How many centimeters are there in 6.5 inches? Round your answer to the nearest tenth.

21. At $1.80 a meter, how much do 3.75 meters of lumber cost?

22. 69.53 ÷ 17 =   23. 2.016 ÷ 0.28 =   24. 14.1 ÷ 2.35 =

25. 9 ÷ 0.036 =   26. 5.13 ÷ 1,000 =

27. A train traveled 145 miles in 4.2 hours. To the nearest tenth, what was the average speed of the train in miles per hour?

28. Manny made $102.05 for 6.5 hours of work. How much did he make per hour?

Cumulative Review Chart

If you missed more than one problem on any group below, review the practice pages for those problems. Then redo the problems you got wrong before going on to the Percent Skills Inventory. If you had a passing score, redo any problem you missed and begin the Percent Skills Inventory on page 96.

PROBLEM NUMBERS	SKILL AREA	PRACTICE PAGES
1, 2, 3, 4	using fractions	11–57
5, 6, 7, 8, 9, 10	understanding decimals	62–72
11, 12, 13	adding decimals	73–74
14, 15, 16	subtracting decimals	75–78
17, 18, 19, 20, 21	multiplying decimals	79–85
22, 23, 24, 25, 26, 27, 28	dividing decimals	86–93

PERCENTS

Percent Skills Inventory

This inventory will let you know whether you need to work through the percent section of this book. Do all the problems that you can. Work carefully and check your answers, but do not use outside help. Correct answers are listed by page number at the back of the book.

1. Write 0.017 as a percent.

2. Write 4% as a decimal.

3. Write $\frac{5}{8}$ as a percent.

4. Write 12% as a proper fraction.

5. Write $8\frac{1}{3}\%$ as a proper fraction.

6. Find 15% of 80.

7. Find 4.6% of 250.

8. Find $37\frac{1}{2}\%$ of 96.

9. The sales tax in Tony's state is 8%. How much tax does he owe for a compact disk that costs $10.50?

10. The Olsons spend $33\frac{1}{3}\%$ of their take-home pay on mortgage payments. If their take-home pay is $1,689 a month, what is their monthly mortgage payment?

11. 15 is what percent of 45?

12. 32 is what percent of 400?

13. On a loan of $500, Alfonso had to pay $55 in interest. The interest represents what percent of the loan?

14. There were 36 people at a meeting of a tenants' organization. The total number of members in the organization is 54. What percent of the members attended the meeting?

15. 75% of what number is 60?

16. $62\frac{1}{2}$% of what number is 35?

17. The Morris family spends $760 a month for rent. If rent represents 25% of their monthly income, what is their monthly income?

18. Chuck spent $1.59 in tax for a new shirt. The tax rate in his state is 6%. What was the price of the shirt?

Percent Skills Inventory Chart

If you missed more than one problem on any group below, work through the practice pages for that group. Then redo the problems you got wrong on the Percent Skills Inventory. If you had a passing score on all four groups of problems, redo any problem you missed and begin Posttest A on page 123 or Posttest B on page 127.

PROBLEM NUMBERS	SKILL AREA	PRACTICE PAGES
1, 2, 3, 4, 5	understanding percents	98–103
6, 7, 8, 9, 10	finding a percent	104–109
11, 12, 13, 14	finding what percent one number is of another	110–113
15, 16, 17, 18	finding a number when a percent is given	115–118

Understanding Percents

Percent is a common term in the business world. Commissions, interest, mark-ups, discounts, credit card charges, and tax rates are all calculated with percent.

Percent is one more way—besides fractions and decimals—of describing a part of a whole. Remember that with fractions, the denominator tells how many parts a whole is divided into. Any whole number except for zero can be a denominator. With decimals a whole is divided into tenths, hundredths, thousandths, ten-thousandths, and so on. Percent is more limited. With percent the whole is always divided into 100 parts. In fact, the word *percent* means "by the hundred or per one hundred." Percent is shown with the sign %.

Think about these examples of percents.

EXAMPLES

35¢ is $\frac{35}{100}$ of a dollar or 0.35 of a dollar or 35% of a dollar

7 is $\frac{1}{2}$ of 14 or 0.5 of 14 or 50% of 14

9 is $\frac{1}{4}$ of 36 or 0.25 of 36 or 25% of 36

If a pizza is cut into eight slices and you have all eight slices, you have $\frac{8}{8}$ of the pizza or 1 whole pizza or 100% of the pizza.

Fill in each blank.

1. Percent means that a whole has been divided into _____ equal parts.

2. 49¢ is $\frac{49}{100}$ of a dollar or _____% of a dollar.

3. 75% of something means 75 of the _____ equal parts of something.

4. If every registered student attends a night class, you can say that _____% of the students are there.

5. If Gloria gets every problem right on a math quiz, you can say that she got _____% of the problems right.

6. If Bernard gets only half of the problems right on a math quiz, you can say that he got _____% of the problems right.

Changing Decimals to Percents

Percent is similar to a two-place decimal. To change a decimal to a percent, move the decimal point two places to the *right* and write the percent sign (%). If the decimal point moves to the end of the number, it is not necessary to write it. You may have to add zeros.

EXAMPLES

Decimal		Percent
0.35	= 0.35	= 35%
0.8	= 0.80	= 80%
0.04	= 0.04	= 4%
$0.12\frac{1}{2}$	= $0.12\frac{1}{2}$	= $12\frac{1}{2}\%$
0.0007	= 0.00 07	= 0.07%

Write each decimal as a percent.

1. 0.32 =   0.09 =   0.6 =   0.136 =

2. 0.005 = $0.37\frac{1}{2}$ = $0.08\frac{1}{3}$ =   0.045 =

3. 0.0016 =   0.0003 =   0.025 = $0.33\frac{1}{3}$ =

4. 0.125 =   0.0375 =   0.009 =   0.2 =

5. See how quickly you can fill in the following tables. You will save time later if you memorize these common decimals and percents.

Decimal	Percent
0.1	
0.3	
0.7	
0.9	

Decimal	Percent
0.2	
0.4	
0.6	
0.8	

Decimal	Percent
0.01	
0.25	
0.5	
0.75	

Changing Percents to Decimals

To change a percent to a decimal, drop the percent sign (%) and move the decimal point two places to the *left*. You may have to add zeros.

EXAMPLES **Percent** **Decimal**

6%	= 06	= 0.06
30%	= 30	= 0.3
150%	= 150	= 1.5
0.9%	= 009	= 0.009
$37\frac{1}{2}\%$	= $37\frac{1}{2}$	= $0.37\frac{1}{2}$

Write each percent as a decimal.

1. 20% =   35% =   8% =   60% =

2. 3.5% =   0.4% =   0.03% =   21.6% =

3. $62\frac{1}{2}\% =$ $6\frac{2}{3}\% =$ 2.8% =   19% =

4. 7% =   1.5% =   200% =   14.2% =

5. See how quickly you can fill in the following tables. You will save time later if you memorize these common percents and decimals.

Percent	Decimal
50%	
25%	
75%	
20%	

Percent	Decimal
5%	
1%	
100%	
80%	

Percent	Decimal
37.5%	
62.5%	
87.5%	
12.5%	

Changing Fractions to Percents

There are two ways to change a fraction to a percent as shown below.

EXAMPLE   Change $\frac{3}{4}$ to a percent.

Method 1 Multiply fraction by 100%.

$$\frac{3}{\underset{1}{\cancel{4}}} \times \frac{\overset{25}{\cancel{100\%}}}{1} = \frac{75\%}{1} = \mathbf{75\%}$$

Method 2 Divide the denominator of the fraction into the numerator and move the point two places to the right.

$$\frac{3}{4} = \begin{array}{r} .75 \\ 4\overline{)3.00} \end{array} = \mathbf{75\%}$$

Write each fraction as a percent.

1. $\frac{2}{5} =$ $\frac{1}{4} =$ $\frac{1}{3} =$ $\frac{3}{8} =$

2. $\frac{6}{25} =$ $\frac{2}{3} =$ $\frac{5}{6} =$ $\frac{1}{8} =$

3. $\frac{9}{10} =$ $\frac{7}{8} =$ $\frac{11}{20} =$ $\frac{5}{12} =$

4. $\frac{1}{6} =$ $\frac{4}{5} =$ $\frac{7}{10} =$ $\frac{1}{12} =$

5. $\frac{5}{8} =$ $\frac{4}{9} =$ $\frac{3}{7} =$ $\frac{9}{20} =$

6. $\frac{4}{25} =$ $\frac{3}{10} =$ $\frac{3}{5} =$ $\frac{9}{50} =$

Changing Percents to Fractions

To change a percent to a fraction, write the percent as a fraction with 100 as the denominator and reduce.

<u>EXAMPLE 1</u> Change 85% to a fraction.

| | STEP 1 | Write the percent as a fraction with 100 as the bottom number. | $\dfrac{85}{100}$ |
| | STEP 2 | Reduce. | $\dfrac{85 \div 5}{100 \div 5} = \dfrac{17}{20}$ |

<u>EXAMPLE 2</u> Change $8\frac{1}{3}$% to a fraction.

	STEP 1	Write the percent as a fraction with 100 as the denominator.	$\dfrac{8\frac{1}{3}}{100}$
	STEP 2	You can rewrite this fraction as a division problem.	$8\frac{1}{3} \div 100$
	STEP 3	Change the mixed number to an improper fraction.	$\dfrac{25}{3} \div \dfrac{100}{1}$
	STEP 4	Invert the divisor and multiply, canceling where possible.	$\dfrac{\overset{1}{\cancel{25}}}{3} \times \dfrac{1}{\underset{4}{\cancel{100}}} = \dfrac{1}{12}$

Write each percent as a common fraction.

1. 35% =   20% = $12\frac{1}{2}$% =   6% =

2. $16\frac{2}{3}$% =   1% =   90% = $37\frac{1}{2}$% =

3. 12% =   99% = $66\frac{2}{3}$% = $4\frac{1}{2}$% =

4. 80% = $33\frac{1}{3}$% =   4% = $8\frac{1}{3}$% =

Common Fractions and Percents

After you have filled in the table on this page, check your answers. Then memorize the table. These are the most common fractions and percents. You will save time later on if you know what each of them is equal to.

Fraction	Percent		Fraction	Percent
$\frac{1}{2} =$	50%		$\frac{1}{8} =$	
$\frac{1}{4} =$			$\frac{3}{8} =$	
$\frac{3}{4} =$			$\frac{5}{8} =$	
			$\frac{7}{8} =$	
$\frac{1}{5} =$			$\frac{1}{10} =$	
$\frac{2}{5} =$			$\frac{3}{10} =$	
$\frac{3}{5} =$			$\frac{7}{10} =$	
$\frac{4}{5} =$			$\frac{9}{10} =$	
$\frac{1}{3} =$			$\frac{1}{6} =$	
$\frac{2}{3} =$			$\frac{5}{6} =$	

Do your work here.

Finding a Percent of a Number

To find a percent of a number, change the percent to a decimal or to a fraction and multiply.

<u>EXAMPLE 1</u> Find 25% of 80.

Method 1

STEP 1 Change the percent to a decimal.

STEP 2 Multiply.

$$25\% = .25$$

$$
\begin{array}{r}
80 \\
\times\ .25 \\
\hline
4\ 00 \\
16\ 0 \\
\hline
20.00 = \mathbf{20}
\end{array}
$$

Method 2

STEP 1 Change the percent to a fraction.

STEP 2 Multiply.

$$25\% = \frac{1}{4}$$

$$\frac{1}{\cancel{4}_{1}} \times \frac{\cancel{80}^{20}}{1} = \frac{20}{1} = \mathbf{20}$$

Use the method that you find easier to solve the following.

1. 5% of 120 =   7% of 965 =   10% of 780 =

2. 20% of 36 =   15% of 50 =   40% of 60 =

3. 75% of 680 =   80% of 500 =   50% of 418 =

4. 35% of 480 =   65% of 620 =   85% of 940 =

5. 2.6% of 390 =   0.8% of 56 =   1.8% of 753 =

If you want to multiply by a complex percent like $16\frac{2}{3}\%$, it is easiest to change the percent to the fraction that it is equal to (from the table on page 103) and then multiply.

EXAMPLE 2 Find $16\frac{2}{3}\%$ of 42.

STEP 1   Change the complex percent to a fraction.

STEP 2   Multiply.

$$16\frac{2}{3}\% = \frac{1}{6}$$

$$\frac{1}{\cancel{6}} \times \frac{\cancel{42}^{7}}{1} = \frac{7}{1} = 7$$

If you do not know the fractional value of a complex percent, multiply by the improper fraction form of the percent, and put the other number over 100.

EXAMPLE 3 Find $6\frac{2}{3}\%$ of 45.

STEP 1   Change the complex percent to an improper fraction.

STEP 2   Put the other number over 100 and multiply.

$$6\frac{2}{3}\% = \frac{20}{3}$$

$$\frac{\cancel{20}^{1}}{\cancel{3}_{1}} \times \frac{\cancel{45}^{15}}{\cancel{100}_{5}} = \frac{15}{5} = 3$$

Solve the following.

6. $33\frac{1}{3}\%$ of 75 = $12\frac{1}{2}\%$ of 96 = $16\frac{2}{3}\%$ of 84 =

7. $37\frac{1}{2}\%$ of 720 = $83\frac{1}{3}\%$ of 630 = $1\frac{1}{2}\%$ of 200 =

8. $5\frac{1}{4}\%$ of 400 = $66\frac{2}{3}\%$ of 90 = $87\frac{1}{2}\%$ of 200 =

9. $8\frac{1}{3}\%$ of 36 = $6\frac{1}{4}\%$ of 60 = $62\frac{1}{2}\%$ of 176 =

Using Shortcuts

Look at the following percent list and the fraction that each percent equals.

50%	$33\frac{1}{3}$%	25%	20%	$16\frac{2}{3}$%	$12\frac{1}{2}$%	10%
$\frac{1}{2}$	$\frac{1}{3}$	$\frac{1}{4}$	$\frac{1}{5}$	$\frac{1}{6}$	$\frac{1}{8}$	$\frac{1}{10}$

Notice that each percent in the list is equal to a fraction with a numerator of 1.

To find a percent of a number with any percent on this list, simply divide by the denominator of the fraction that the percent equals (Method 3 below).

EXAMPLE   What is 25% of 120?

Method 1 $0.25 \times 120 = 30.00 = \mathbf{30}$

Method 2 $\frac{1}{\cancel{4}_{1}} \times \frac{\cancel{120}^{30}}{1} = \frac{30}{1} = \mathbf{30}$

Method 3 $120 \div 4 = \mathbf{30}$

The shortcut Method 3 is the same as the canceling step from Method 2.

Use the shortcut method to solve each of the following problems in your head.

1. 50% of 48 = $33\frac{1}{3}$% of 690 =   20% of 35 =

2. $12\frac{1}{2}$% of 720 =   10% of 1,300 = $16\frac{2}{3}$% of 240 =

3. 20% of 450 =   25% of 1,600 = $33\frac{1}{3}$% of 90 =

4. 10% of 170 = $12\frac{1}{2}$% of 560 =   20% of 1,500 =

5. $16\frac{2}{3}$% of 720 =   50% of 482 =   25% of 3,600 =

Finding a Percent of a Number: Applying Your Skills

When you find a *percent of* a number, you find a *part of* that number.

Solve and write the correct label, such as $ or pounds, next to each answer.

1. During a period of 30 working days, Deborah was late 80% of the time. How many days was she late?

2. For selling his studio apartment, Martin had to pay the real estate agent a commission of 5%. The studio sold for $95,000. What was the agent's commission?

3. There were 40 questions on the job application that Linda filled out. She had to write N/A for "not applicable" on 15% of the questions. For how many questions did Linda write N/A?

4. A local electricians' union has 540 members. If 65% of the members attended the last meeting, how many members went to the meeting?

5. Doreen's night class was supposed to meet 30 times. Because of snow emergencies, 20% of the classes were canceled. How many of Doreen's classes were canceled?

6. The Smiths spend $33\frac{1}{3}$% of their take-home pay for food. If they take home $504 a week, how much do they spend each week for food?

7. Calvin made a down payment of $12\frac{1}{2}$% on a used car that cost $2,400. How much was the down payment?

8. Joe was supposed to work 250 days last year. He was absent 4% of the time because he was sick. How many days of work did he miss?

9. Ruby used to weigh 150 pounds. She went on a diet and lost 6.5% of her weight. How many pounds did she lose?

Solving Two-Step Problems

Many applications of finding a percent of a number require two steps. First, find the percent of the number. Then add it to or subtract it from the original number. For example, in the last problem, to find Ruby's new weight, subtract the amount she lost from her original weight.

Read each problem carefully to decide whether to add or subtract in the second step.

1. For problem 9 on page 107, what was Ruby's weight after she went on her diet?

2. A jacket originally selling for $48 was on sale at 20% off. Find the sale price of the jacket.

3. For lunch Brian bought a sandwich for $2.50. The sales tax where Brian lives is 6%. What was the price of the sandwich including sales tax?

4. Paul's part-time job earns him $360 each week. His employer withholds 18% of Paul's pay for taxes and social security. How much does Paul take home each week?

5. Elizabeth earns $576 each week. If she gets an 8% raise, how much will she take home each week?

6. The Chan family bought their house for $108,000. They sold it 10 years later for 22% more than they paid. For how much did they sell their house?

7. Kate gets a 15% discount on the price of any item in the clothing store where she works. How much will she pay for a dress that is priced at $58?

8. At the last census, the population of Franklin County was 1.2 million people. At the next census, the population of the county is expected to increase by 10%. What will be the new population of Franklin County?

9. A computer that sold for $1,200 last year is now on sale for 15% less. What is the price of the computer this year?

Using a Calculator

A calculator is a useful tool for getting quick, exact answers. The ⬚% key automatically puts two decimal places in an answer.

EXAMPLE   Use a calculator to find 8.5% of 700.

Press the following keys on a calculator.
[7] [0] [0] [×] [8] [.] [5] [%]

The calculator display should read [59.5].

Note: On some calculators you may have to press the [=] key after the [%] key.

Use a calculator to solve each problem. Read the problems carefully to decide whether they are one-step or two-step problems. Round money answers to the nearest cent.

1. Evelyn has an old balance of $1,300 on her credit card. The credit card company charges 1.75% interest each month. Find the monthly interest on Evelyn's old balance.

2. Of the 2,500 people who were interviewed, 8.2% said that they were undecided about whether the government should increase the military budget. How many of the people interviewed were undecided?

3. A souvenir T-shirt costs $12.49. What is the price of the shirt including 6% sales tax?

4. A pair of winter boots originally selling for $79.90 was on sale for 15% off. Find the sale price of the boots.

5. Of the 320 employees in the factory where Manuel works, 85% participate in the company savings plan. How many employees do *not* participate in the plan?

6. The day Gus's Coffee Shop opened there were 80 diners for lunch. The next day, the number of lunchtime diners increased by 65%. How many people had lunch at Gus's on the second day?

Finding What Percent One Number Is of Another

To find what percent one number is of another, make a fraction by putting the part (usually the smaller number) over the whole. Reduce the fraction and change it to a percent.

EXAMPLE   9 is what percent of 45?

STEP 1 Put the part over the whole and reduce.	$\dfrac{9}{45} = \dfrac{1}{5}$
STEP 2 Divide the denominator into the numerator (see page 101).	$\dfrac{0.20}{5\overline{)1.00}}$
STEP 3 Change the decimal answer to a percent by moving the decimal point two places to the right and adding a percent (%) sign.	$0.20 = \mathbf{20\%}$

Solve the following.

1. 8 is what percent of 16?   15 is what percent of 60?   27 is what percent of 81?

2. 9 is what percent of 90?   12 is what percent of 72?   40 is what percent of 320?

3. 16 is what percent of 20?   14 is what percent of 35?   32 is what percent of 48?

4. 75 is what percent of 90?   33 is what percent of 44?   56 is what percent of 64?

5. 35 is what percent of 40?   45 is what percent of 50?   160 is what percent of 200?

6. 14 is what percent of 200?   24 is what percent of 400?   45 is what percent of 500?

7. 7 is what percent of 20?   19 is what percent of 50?   8 is what percent of 25?

8. 21 is what percent of 36?   19 is what percent of 19?   12 is what percent of 27?

9. 60 is what percent of 72?   24 is what percent of 56?   126 is what percent of 140?

10. 4 is what percent of 200?   18 is what percent of 300?   12 is what percent of 144?

11. 15 is what percent of 75?   84 is what percent of 105?   27 is what percent of 120?

12. 12 is what percent of 72?   2,600 is what percent of 10,000?   792 is what percent of 200,000?

Finding What Percent One Number Is of Another: Applying Your Skills

To find what percent one number is of another, remember to put the *part* over the *whole*. Then change the fraction to a percent.

Solve and write the correct label, such as $ or pounds, next to each answer.

1. There are 24 members in a community block association. Only 18 of them came to their winter meeting. What percent of the members attended the meeting?

2. Joaquin makes $600 a week. A raise of $24 a week represents what percent of his salary?

3. Floria wants to buy a dress that costs $96. She has saved $60 for the dress. What percent of the price of the dress has she saved?

4. Matthew got 36 problems right out of a total of 40 problems on a test. What percent of the problems did he get right?

5. On a loan of $3,500, Manny had to pay $280 interest. The interest was what percent of Manny's loan?

6. Carl weighed 180 pounds. After two months of dieting and exercising, he lost 9 pounds. What percent of his weight did he lose?

7. Margaret is reading a book that is 288 pages long. If she has already read 96 pages, what percent of the book has she read?

8. In the last problem, what percent of the book does Margaret have left to read? (**Hint:** Think of the whole book as 100%.)

9. The Johnson family spends $675 a month on rent. If their monthly income is $2,700, what percent of their income goes to rent?

10. In an office with 20 employees, there are 11 men. What percent of the office workers are men?

11. In the last problem, what percent of the office workers are women?

12. Carlos owed $2,000 to the bank. If he has paid back $1,250, what percent of the amount that he owes has he paid back?

13. The price of a dozen large eggs went up $0.09 from $1.08. The increase represents what percent of the original price?

14. The Rivera family makes $720 a week. If they spend $180 each week for food, what percent of their income goes for food?

15. For the Rivera family in the last problem, what percent of their weekly income is left for all expenses except food?

16. George bought a used car last year for $3,520. This year it is worth $440 less. The decrease in value represents what percent of the price George paid?

17. Last year the population of Middleville was 16,000 people. In one year the population has increased by 800 people. The increase represents what percent of last year's population?

18. Rachel belongs to a car pool. She has driven her car to work 8 days out of the past 48. What percent of that time did she drive her car to work?

19. An inch represents what percent of a foot?

20. A foot is what percent of a yard?

Finding a Percent of Change

A common application of percent is to find a percent of change. First, find the amount of the change. Next, make a fraction with the change over the original (earlier) amount. Finally, change that fraction to a percent.

EXAMPLE   The price of a jacket dropped from \$30 to \$24. By what percent did the price drop?

STEP 1   Find the amount of the change.   \$30 − \$24 = \$6

STEP 2   Make a fraction with the change over the original $\dfrac{\$6}{\$30} = \dfrac{1}{5}$
amount and reduce.

STEP 3   Change $\dfrac{1}{5}$ to a percent. $\dfrac{1}{5} = 20\%$

Solve each problem. Remember to write the amount of change over the original amount.

1. A color TV that originally sold for \$380 was on sale for \$285. By what percent was the original price discounted?

2. Anna's weekly salary is \$500, but she takes home only \$395. The deductions her employer takes out are what percent of her weekly salary?

3. At the beginning of the football season, 800 people attended a high school game. After the team lost several games, the attendance was down to 560 people. By what percent did the attendance drop?

4. Last year a town budget was \$2.4 million. This year the budget will be \$2.7 million. By what percent did the budget increase from last year?

5. Mr. Park pays a distributor \$210 for a compact stereo system. He charges his customers \$280 for the system. The markup is what percent of the price Mr. Park pays the distributor?

6. The Lincoln family bought their house in 1973 for \$28,000. They sold the house in 1999 for \$140,000. By what percent did the value of the house increase?

Finding a Number When a Percent of It Is Given

If a percent of a number is given and you are looking for the whole number, change the percent into either a fraction or a decimal and divide it into the number you have.

EXAMPLE   20% of what number is 16?

Method 1

STEP 1   Change the percent to a fraction.

STEP 2   Divide the number you have by the fraction.

$20\% = \dfrac{1}{5}$

$16 \div \dfrac{1}{5} = \dfrac{16}{1} \times \dfrac{5}{1} = \dfrac{80}{1} = \mathbf{80}$

Method 2

STEP 1   Change the percent to a decimal.

STEP 2   Divide the number you have by the decimal.

$20\% = 0.2$

$$0.2\overline{)16.0} \quad \overset{8\,0.}{}$$

Use the method you find easier to solve the following.

1. 25% of what number is 8?   50% of what number is 45?

2. 75% of what number is 48?   60% of what number is 75?

3. 40% of what number is 60?   15% of what number is 12?

4. 10% of what number is 6.3?   35% of what number is 8.4?

5. $33\frac{1}{3}$% of what number is 25? $12\frac{1}{2}$% of what number is 160?

6. $16\frac{2}{3}$% of what number is 300?   8.5% of what number is 119?

7. $37\frac{1}{2}$% of what number is 24? $83\frac{1}{3}$% of what number is 150?

8. $66\frac{2}{3}$% of what number is 320? $87\frac{1}{2}$% of what number is 210?

9. $62\frac{1}{2}$% of what number is 120?   12.6% of what number is 189?

10. 80% of what number is 244? $33\frac{1}{3}$% of what number is 350?

11. $83\frac{1}{3}$% of what number is 365?   20% of what number is 175?

Finding a Number When a Percent of It Is Given: Applying Your Skills

In these word problems, you have a *part* and a percent rate. You are looking for the *whole*. Change the percent to either a decimal or a fraction. Then divide into the part you have. If the percent rate in the problem is less than 100%, your answer (the whole) will be larger than the part.

Solve and write the correct label, such as $ or pounds, next to each answer.

1. Morris has saved $80 toward the purchase of a new VCR. The $80 is 50% of the price. What is the price of the VCR?

2. Lois got 27 problems right on a math test. If this is 90% of the test, how many problems were on the test?

3. Pat made a down payment of $500 on a used car. The $500 is 20% of the price of the car. Find the price of the car.

4. There were 130 people in a school auditorium to listen to a political candidate. This represents $33\frac{1}{3}$% of the capacity of the auditorium. How many seats are in the auditorium?

5. Phil had to pay $4.80 in tax for a new pair of pants. If the sales tax in Phil's state is 8%, what was the price of the pants?

6. There are 78 members at a club meeting. If they represented 65% of the total membership, how many members does the club have?

7. Mavis made $145 in commissions one week for selling shoes. Her commission rate is 5% of the total amount that she sells. What was the value of the shoes she sold that week?

8. When the Greens bought their house, they made a down payment of $18,000, which was 15% of the total price of the house. Find the price of the house.

9. Sonia works in quality control at a factory that makes car radios. One week she found 18 defective radios. This represents 0.8% of the number of radios produced. How many radios did the factory produce that week?

10. Last week 3,000 people came to hear a presidential candidate speak in Central City. If they represent $16\frac{2}{3}$% of the people who live in Central City, how many people live there?

11. David has driven 2,550 miles on his way from New York to San Francisco. If he has driven 85% of the total distance, what is the distance from New York to San Francisco?

12. Tom had to pay $240 in interest on a loan. The interest was 12% of the total loan. How much was the loan?

13. Mr. Moore pays $21 to a supplier for the hand drills he sells in his hardware store. $21 is 60% of the price he charges his customers. How much does Mr. Moore charge for a hand drill at his store?

14. Walter's weekly take-home pay is $354.90, which is 78% of his gross pay (before deductions). What is Walter's weekly gross pay?

15. In the last problem, what are the weekly deductions from Walter's gross pay?

Recognizing Types of Percent Problems

In the statement, "6 is 20% of 30," the number 6 is the *part*, the number 30 is the *whole*, and 20% is the *percent*. Three problems can be made from these numbers.

EXAMPLE 1   *Finding the part:* What is 20% of 30?

This is the most common type of percent problem.

To solve Example 1, change the percent to a fraction or a decimal and *multiply* by the *whole*.

$20\% = 0.2$
$0.2 \times 30 = \mathbf{6}$

EXAMPLE 2   *Finding the percent:* 6 is what percent of 30?

This is the easiest type of percent problem to recognize. The percent is not given.

To solve Example 2, make a fraction with the *part* over the *whole* and change the fraction to a percent.

$\dfrac{6}{30} = \dfrac{1}{5} = \mathbf{20\%}$

EXAMPLE 3   *Finding the whole:* 20% of what number is 6?

This is the least common type of percent problem.

To solve Example 3, change the percent to a decimal or a fraction and *divide* into the *part*.

$20\% = 0.2$

$$0.2\overline{)6.0} \quad \mathbf{30.}$$

Next to each problem, write *P* for finding the part, % for finding the percent, or *W* for finding the whole. Then solve each problem.

1. 18 is what percent of 36?   What is 30% of 110?

2. Find $12\frac{1}{2}$% of 720.   What percent of 50 is 10?

3. 15 is 25% of what number?   What is 85% of 400?

4. What is $37\frac{1}{2}$% of 40?   48 is what percent of 60?

5. What percent of 60 is 20?   230 is 50% of what number?

6. Of the 500 employees at Ajax Electronics, only 6% go to work by public transportation. How many employees at Ajax use public transportation to get to work?

7. The Moore family expects to spend $1,200 on their summer vacation. So far they have saved $900 toward their vacation. What percent of the cost have they saved?

8. The sales tax rate in Linda's state is 5%. How much tax does she have to pay on a shirt that costs $29?

9. Juan saves 10% of his take-home pay. He puts $160 in his savings account each month. What is his monthly take-home pay?

10. The total bill for Paul and Dorothy's dinner was $32. They left a tip of $4.80. The tip was what percent of the total bill?

11. Of the 360 people who took a qualifying exam for an inspector's job, 55% of the people passed. How many people passed?

12. A school sold 1,020 tickets for a benefit concert. The ticket sales were 85% of the seating capacity of the school auditorium. How many seats are there in the auditorium?

Cumulative Review

This review covers the material you have studied so far in this book. When you finish, check your answers at the back of the book.

1. $4\frac{5}{8} + 9\frac{1}{4} =$

2. $12 - 7\frac{3}{5} =$

3. $5\frac{1}{4} \times \frac{1}{3} =$

4. Round 1.297 to the nearest hundredth.

5. $0.25 \times 1.3 =$

6. Find $4.6 \div 3$ to the nearest tenth.

7. Write 0.123 as a percent.

8. Write 5.6% as a decimal.

9. Write $\frac{7}{12}$ as a percent.

10. Write 84% as a fraction.

11. Write $31\frac{1}{4}\%$ as a fraction.

12. Find 9% of 270.

13. Find 11.3% of 460.

14. Which of the following is the same as $12\frac{1}{2}\%$ of 72?
    a. $72 \div 4$
    b. $72 \div 6$
    c. $72 \div 8$
    d. $72 \div 12$

15. Bill works at an electronics store. He gets a 15% discount on equipment sold in the store. How much can he save on a VCR that sells for $165?

16. There are 24,000 registered voters in Millville. If only $37\frac{1}{2}\%$ of them voted in the last election, how many of the registered voters did *not* vote?

17. 45 is what percent of 72?

18. 17 is what percent of 200?

19. The Millers want to buy a house trailer for which the down payment is $5,000. They have already saved $3,750. What percent of the down payment have they saved?

20. Of the 32 employees in an office, 20 of them are women. What percent of the employees are women?

21. 40% of what number is 80?

22. $12\frac{1}{2}$% of what number is 48?

23. Alfredo has driven 273 miles, which is 65% of the total distance he has to drive. Find the total distance he has to drive.

24. By Thursday, the cutters and sewers in a clothing factory had made 280 jackets. This is $87\frac{1}{2}$% of the total number of jackets they were expected to make for the week. What is the total number of jackets the workers had to make that week?

Cumulative Review Chart

If you missed more than one problem on any group below, review the practice pages for those problems. Then redo the problems you got wrong before going on to Posttest A or B. If you had a passing score, redo any problem you missed and begin Posttest A on page 123 or Posttest B on page 128.

PROBLEM NUMBERS	SKILL AREA	PRACTICE PAGES
1, 2, 3	using fractions	11–57
4, 5, 6	using decimals	62–93
7, 8, 9, 10, 11	understanding percents	98–103
12, 13, 14, 15, 16	finding a percent	104–109
17, 18, 19, 20	finding what percent one number is of another	110–113
21, 22, 23, 24	finding a number when a percent is given	115–118

Posttest A

This posttest gives you a chance to check your understanding of fractions, decimals and percents. Take your time and work each problem carefully. When you finish, check your answers and review any topics on which you need more work.

1. Reduce $\frac{16}{36}$ to lowest terms.

2. $5\frac{7}{8} + 4\frac{2}{3} + 9\frac{1}{2} =$

3. Is the sum of $\frac{5}{16} + \frac{7}{15}$ greater than 1, less than 1, or equal to 1?

4. A table that is $46\frac{1}{2}$ inches long can be made longer with an insert that is $12\frac{2}{3}$ inches long. How long is the table with the insert?

5. $23\frac{2}{9} + 18\frac{3}{4} =$

6. A copper pipe that is $75\frac{1}{4}$ inches long is how much longer than a pipe that is $68\frac{5}{16}$ inches long?

7. $\frac{5}{6} \times \frac{8}{15} \times \frac{3}{20} =$

8. $4\frac{1}{2} \times 2\frac{2}{5} \times 3\frac{3}{4} =$

9. In the problem $4\frac{1}{3} \times 5\frac{7}{8}$, first round each number to the nearest whole number. Then multiply.

10. A plumber charges $29 for an hour of work. How much would he charge for a job that took him $1\frac{3}{4}$ hours to finish?

11. $\frac{3}{5} \div 15 =$

12. $4\frac{2}{3} \div 1\frac{1}{9} =$

13. How many $\frac{3}{4}$-pound bags of sugar can be filled with 36 pounds of sugar?

14. Henry wants to buy a new table saw for his carpentry shop. He has saved $360, which is $\frac{2}{3}$ of the price of the saw. How much does the table saw cost?

15. Write fifty and two hundred eight thousandths as a mixed decimal.

16. Write the following decimals in order from smallest to largest:
    0.021, 0.12, 0.2, 0.02

17. $293.08 + 14 + 2.719 =$

18. Mary weighed 119.3 pounds in September. By January 1, she weighed 8.8 pounds more. What was her weight on January 1?

19. $40 - 0.387 =$

20. In the problem $19.28 - 1.546$, first round each number to the nearest *tenth*. Then subtract.

21. The Rodriguez family need to drive 250 miles to visit their cousins. If they have already driven 113.8 miles, how much farther do they need to drive?

22. $2.048 \times 1.9 =$

23. In the problem 67.4×0.08, first round 67.4 to the nearest *ten*. Then multiply.

24. Find the cost of 4.8 kilograms of potatoes at the price of $0.75 a kilogram?

25. $1.274 \div 4.9 =$

26. $0.3474 \div 0.018 =$

27. Find the answer to $24 \div 1.7$ to the nearest tenth.

28. There are 1.6 kilometers in a mile. Find the distance in miles between two towns that are 24 kilometers apart.

29. Write 7.9% as a decimal.

30. Write $\frac{9}{16}$ as a percent.

31. Write $16\frac{2}{3}\%$ as a common fraction.

32. Find 18% of 304.

33. Find $8\frac{1}{3}\%$ of 144.

34. Which of the following is the same as 25% of 84?

    a. $84 \div 5$
    b. $84 \div 4$
    c. $84 \div 3$
    d. $84 \div 2$

35. Mike gets an 8% commission on the sporting goods that he sells. One day he sold sporting goods worth $1,384. Find his commission for that day.

36. 75 is what percent of 90?

37. Sandy owed the bank $1,200. She has already paid back $750. What percent of the money that she owed has she paid back to the bank?

38. 35% of what number is 56?

39. A community has raised $200,000 for its summer youth program. This amount is 80% of the total they need. What is the total cost of the summer youth program?

Posttest A Prescriptions

Circle the number of any problem that you miss. If you missed one or less in each group below, go on to Using Number Power. If you missed more than one problem in any group, review the pages in this book or refer to these practice pages in other materials from Contemporary Books.

PROBLEM NUMBERS	PRESCRIPTION MATERIALS	PRACTICE PAGES
1, 2, 3, 4, 5, 6, 7, 8, 9, 10, 11, 12, 13, 14	using fractions	11–57
	Math Exercises: Fractions	3–29
	Breakthroughs in Math: Book 2	66–113
	Math Skills That Work: Book Two	70–103
	Real Numbers: Fractions and Percents	1–38
	Critical Thinking with Math	78–91
15, 16, 17, 18, 19, 20, 21, 22, 23, 24, 25, 26, 27, 28	using decimals	62–93
	Math Exercises: Decimals	3–29
	Breakthroughs in Math, Book 2	34–65
	Math Skills That Work, Book Two	32–67
	Real Numbers: Whole Numbers and Decimals	37–69
	Critical Thinking with Math	66–77
29, 30, 31, 32, 33, 34, 35, 36, 37, 38, 39	using percents	98–120
	Math Exercises: Percents	3–29
	Breakthroughs in Math: Book 2	114–141
	Math Skills That Work, Book Two	106–137
	Real Numbers: Fractions and Percents	39–68
	Critical Thinking with Math	92–104

For further practice:

Basic Skills/Pre-GED Interactive (software)
    Mathematics Units 2, 3, 7

Math Solutions (software)
    Fractions; Decimals; Percents, Ratios, Proportions

GED Interactive (software)
    Mathematics Units 2, 3, 4

Posttest B

This review test has a multiple-choice format much like the GED and other standardized tests. Take your time and work each problem carefully. Circle the correct answer to each problem. When you finish, check your answers at the back of the book.

1. Reduce $\frac{36}{54}$ to lowest terms.

   a. $\frac{3}{7}$ b. $\frac{3}{5}$ c. $\frac{2}{3}$ d. $\frac{2}{5}$

2. $5\frac{3}{16} + 4\frac{2}{3} + 6\frac{1}{2} =$

   a. $16\frac{17}{48}$ b. $16\frac{9}{16}$ c. $15\frac{7}{48}$ d. $15\frac{3}{16}$

3. Which of the following best describes the sum of $\frac{5}{9} + \frac{8}{15}$?

   a. greater than 1   b. less than 1   c. equal to 1   d. less than 0

4. Find the combined weight of a motor that weighs $48\frac{5}{16}$ pounds and a wooden packing crate that weighs $3\frac{3}{4}$ pounds.

   a. $49\frac{7}{16}$ pounds   b. $60\frac{1}{16}$ pounds   c. $51\frac{7}{16}$ pounds   d. $52\frac{1}{16}$ pounds

5. $8\frac{1}{3} - 3\frac{4}{5} =$

   a. $5\frac{7}{15}$ b. $5\frac{2}{15}$ c. $4\frac{8}{15}$ d. $4\frac{4}{15}$

6. A door opening is 68 inches high, and Jason is $62\frac{1}{2}$ inches tall. How much taller is the door frame than Jason?

   a. $4\frac{1}{2}$ inches   b. $5\frac{1}{2}$ inches   c. $6\frac{1}{2}$ inches   d. $7\frac{1}{2}$ inches

7. $\frac{9}{16} \times \frac{2}{3} =$

   a. $\frac{7}{16}$ b. $\frac{3}{16}$ c. $\frac{7}{8}$ d. $\frac{3}{8}$

8. $2\frac{1}{4} \times \frac{2}{3} \times 1\frac{5}{6} =$

    a. $3\frac{1}{4}$
        b. $2\frac{3}{4}$
        c. $2\frac{5}{6}$
        d. $1\frac{5}{6}$

9. In the problem $1\frac{7}{8} \times 6\frac{5}{6}$, first round each number to the nearest whole number. Then multiply.

    a. 6
        b. 7
        c. 12
        d. 14

10. What is the total weight of three packages of grass seed, if each weighs $1\frac{3}{4}$ pounds?

    a. $5\frac{1}{4}$ pounds
        b. $4\frac{3}{4}$ pounds
        c. $4\frac{1}{4}$ pounds
        d. $3\frac{3}{4}$ pounds

11. $3\frac{1}{5} \div 4 =$

    a. $\frac{3}{4}$
        b. $\frac{3}{5}$
        c. $\frac{4}{5}$
        d. $1\frac{1}{5}$

12. $2\frac{2}{3} \div 1\frac{1}{9} =$

    a. $1\frac{3}{5}$
        b. $1\frac{4}{5}$
        c. $2\frac{1}{5}$
        d. $2\frac{2}{5}$

13. How many bags, each containing $1\frac{3}{4}$ pounds of topsoil, can be filled from a pile of soil that weighs 350 pounds?

    a. 130 bags
        b. 150 bags
        c. 175 bags
        d. 200 bags

14. Laurie is getting signatures on a petition. So far she has 240 signatures. This is $\frac{3}{4}$ of her goal. How many signatures is she trying to get?

    a. 320
        b. 300
        c. 280
        d. 250

15. What is seven and fifty-one thousandths written as a mixed decimal?

    a. 75.1
        b. 7.51
        c. 7.051
        d. 7.0051

16. Write the following decimals in order from smallest to largest:
0.06, 0.064, 0.4, 0.004

  a. 0.004, 0.4, 0.064, 0.06   **c.** 0.06, 0.4, 0.004, 0.064
  b. 0.004, 0.06, 0.064, 0.4   **d.** 0.06, 0.064, 0.004, 0.4

17. $3.49 + 8 + 14.902 =$

  a. 24.61   **b.** 24.402   **c.** 26.392   **d.** 26.41

18. In the year 2000, the population of the earth is 6.09 billion. Experts think the population in 2020 will be 1.503 billion more than in 2000. What is the population of the earth expected to be in 2020?

  a. 7.093 billion   **b.** 7.593 billion   **c.** 6.593 billion   **d.** 6.093 billion

19. $32 - 19.786 =$

  a. 19.754   **b.** 19.466   **c.** 12.786   **d.** 12.214

20. In the problem $2.749 - 0.1847$, first round each number to the nearest *hundredth*. Then subtract.

  a. 2.57   **b.** 2.92   **c.** 4.4   **d.** 9.02

21. One yard is equal to 0.914 meter. A meter is how much longer than one yard?

  a. 0.014 meter   **b.** 0.086 meter   **c.** 0.114 meter   **d.** 0.186 meter

22. $17.6 \times 3.09 =$

  a. 54.384   **b.** 5.4384   **c.** 0.54384   **d.** 543.84

23. In the problem 60.8×0.4, first round 60.8 to the nearest *unit*. Then multiply.

  a. 240   **b.** 24   **c.** 24.4   **d.** 24.48

24. Find the cost of 1.7 pounds of cheese at a cost of $4.98 per pound. Round your answer to the nearest cent.

  a. $6.68   **b.** $7.47   **c.** $7.68   **d.** $8.47

25. $39.56 \div 9.2 =$

    a. 0.23   **b.** 2.3   **c.** 4.3   **d.** 43

26. $6 \div 1.5 =$

    a. 40   **b.** 4   **c.** 2.5   **d.** 0.25

27. Find the answer to $7.85 \div 1.2$ to the nearest *hundredth*.

    a. 65.41   **b.** 15.29   **c.** 6.54   **d.** 0.65

28. Carla drove 144 miles in 2.5 hours. To the nearest unit, find her average speed in miles per hour.

    a. 50 mph   **b.** 52 mph   **c.** 55 mph   **d.** 58 mph

29. Write 2.6% as a decimal.

    a. 2.6   **b.** 0.26   **c.** 0.026   **d.** 0.0026

30. Write $\frac{3}{7}$ as a percent.

    a. $42\frac{6}{7}\%$ **b.** $39\frac{5}{7}\%$ **c.** $23\frac{1}{3}\%$ **d.** $4\frac{2}{7}\%$

31. Write $31\frac{1}{4}\%$ as a common fraction.

    a. $\frac{5}{8}$ **b.** $\frac{5}{9}$ **c.** $\frac{5}{12}$ **d.** $\frac{5}{16}$

32. Find 42% of 700.

    a. 2.94   **b.** 29.4   **c.** 294   **d.** 2,940

33. Find $87\frac{1}{2}\%$ of 240.

    a. 21   **b.** 30   **c.** 180   **d.** 210

34. Which of the following is the same as $16\frac{2}{3}\%$ of 180?

    a. $180 \div 2$ **b.** $180 \div 4$ **c.** $180 \div 6$ **d.** $180 \div 8$

35. 84 is what percent of 96?

   a. $87\frac{1}{2}\%$ **b.** 84%   **c.** 45%   **d.** $62\frac{1}{2}\%$

36. One year a community college offered a course in furnace maintenance. That year 24 students registered for the class. When the college offered the class the next year, 42 students registered. By what percent did the number of registrations increase?

   a. 25%   **b.** 51%   **c.** 60%   **d.** 75%

37. 65% of what number is 78?

   a. 51   **b.** 90   **c.** 120   **d.** 186

38. At the Central School night program, 196 students said that they planned to go on to further study. They represent 70% of the total number of students. How many students are in the night program?

   a. 296   **b.** 280   **c.** 226   **d.** 137

Posttest B Chart

If you missed more than one problem on any group below, review the practice pages for those problems. Then redo the problems you got wrong before going on to Using Number Power. If you had a passing score, redo any problem you missed and go on to Using Number Power on page 133.

PROBLEM NUMBERS	SKILL AREA	PRACTICE PAGES
1, 2, 3, 4, 5, 6, 7, 8, 9, 10, 11, 12, 13, 14	using fractions	11–57
15, 16, 17, 18, 19, 20, 21, 22, 23, 24, 25, 26, 27, 28	using decimals	62–93
29, 30, 31, 32, 33, 34, 35, 36, 37, 38	using percents	98–120

Using
Number
Power

Reading a Ruler

The six-inch ruler shown on this page is divided into inches (at the numbers), half inches (every eight lines), quarter inches (every four lines), eighth inches (every other line), and sixteenth inches (from one line to the next).

Remember that rulers, like books, are read from left to right. The arrow at A is $\frac{1}{2}$ inch from the left end of the ruler. The arrow at B is $1\frac{3}{8}$ inches from the left end.

Use the ruler above to answer the following questions.

1. Tell in inches how far from the left end each of the following points is.

   C   H

   D   I

   E   J

   F   K

   G   L

2. How much farther is point D from the left end of the ruler than point C?

3. How much farther is point H from the left end of the ruler than point F?

4. How much farther is point L from the left end of the ruler than point J?

Reading a Metric Ruler

The sixteen-centimeter ruler shown on this page is divided into centimeters (at the numbers) and millimeters at each line. There are ten millimeters in a centimeter. Every fifth millimeter is a longer mark on the ruler.

The arrow at A is 5 millimeters or 0.5 centimeters from the left end of the ruler. The arrow at B is 1.3 centimeters from the left end.

Use the ruler above to answer the following questions.

1. Tell in centimeters how far from the left end each of the following points is.

   C   H

   D   I

   E   J

   F   K

   G   L

2. How much farther is point E from the left end of the ruler than point C?

3. How much farther is point G from the left end of the ruler than point F?

4. How much farther is point K from the left end of the ruler than point J?

Finding the Perimeter of Rectangles and Squares

When you measure the distance around something, you are finding its **perimeter.** You can find this distance (perimeter) by measuring each side and adding all the measurements together. If you want to find the perimeter of something with two pairs of equal sides (a **rectangle**), you can double the length (the long sides), double the width (the short sides), and add these two answers. This rule can be written in a short form called a formula: $P = 2l + 2w$. P stands for perimeter, l stands for length, and w stands for width.

EXAMPLE   How much tape do you need to go around the edges of a rectangle with a length of $4\frac{3}{4}$ inches and a width of $2\frac{1}{2}$ inches?

STEP 1 $2 \times 4\frac{3}{4} = \frac{\cancel{2}^{1}}{1} \times \frac{19}{\cancel{4}_{2}} = \frac{19}{2} = 9\frac{1}{2}$ inches

STEP 2 $2 \times 2\frac{1}{2} = \frac{\cancel{2}^{1}}{1} \times \frac{5}{\cancel{2}_{1}} = 5$ inches

STEP 3 $9\frac{1}{2}$ inches
$\underline{+\ 5}$ inches
$14\frac{1}{2}$ inches

$4\frac{3}{4}''$
$2\frac{1}{2}''$ $2\frac{1}{2}''$
$4\frac{3}{4}''$

Solve each problem. Be sure to label each answer.

1. How much tape do you need to go around the edges of a rectangle $7\frac{2}{3}$ inches long and 3 inches wide?

2. How much weather stripping will you need to go around a window that is $6\frac{7}{8}$ feet long and $2\frac{1}{4}$ feet wide.

3. How many inches of picture frame molding are needed to go around a picture that is 11 inches long and $8\frac{1}{2}$ inches wide?

4. Mr. King's garden is 6.2 meters long and 5.8 meters wide. How many meters of fencing are needed to enclose the garden?

5. If fencing costs $9.50 per meter, how much would the fencing for the garden in problem 4 cost?

6. Find the perimeter of a tabletop that is $62\frac{1}{2}$ inches long and $30\frac{1}{4}$ inches wide.

7. What is the perimeter of a photograph that is 10.3 centimeters long and 4.6 centimeters wide?

8. How much fencing would be needed to enclose a garden that measures $6\frac{1}{4}$ yards on every side?

9. Find the perimeter of a snapshot that measures $2\frac{1}{2}$ inches on each side.

10. What is the perimeter of a piece of tile that measures 1.75 meters on every side?

Finding the Area of Rectangles and Squares

When you buy carpeting, you have to know how much space you want to cover. To figure out the answer to problems like this, you need to find **area.** Area is the amount of space or surface of a flat figure like a floor. Area is measured in square inches, square feet, square yards, and so on. To find the area of a rectangle, you multiply the length by the width. The formula is $A = lw$. A stands for the area, l stands for the length, and w stands for the width. Notice that l and w written next to each other means that they should be multiplied together.

EXAMPLE   How much shelf paper do you need to cover a shelf that is $4\frac{1}{2}$ feet long and $1\frac{1}{4}$ feet wide?

$$4\frac{1}{2} \times 1\frac{1}{4} = \frac{9}{2} \times \frac{5}{4} = \frac{45}{8} = 5\frac{5}{8} \text{ square feet}$$

Solve each problem. Be sure to label each answer in square units.

1. How much glass do you need to cover a coffee table that is $5\frac{1}{3}$ feet long and $3\frac{3}{4}$ feet wide?

2. How much space is covered by a tile that is 6.2 centimeters long and 2.8 centimeters wide?

3. How many square inches of plastic are needed to cover a photograph that is $7\frac{1}{2}$ inches long and 4 inches wide?

4. How many square feet are in a flower garden that is 14 feet long and 2 feet wide?

5. Find the area of a floor that is 7.2 meters long and 5.5 meters wide.

6. If one square meter of carpet costs $16.40, how much would the carpet cost to cover the floor in problem 5?

7. How many square yards of carpeting are needed to cover the floor of a room that is $3\frac{1}{3}$ yards long and $2\frac{1}{4}$ yards wide?

8. How much space can you cover with a piece of linoleum that measures 3.6 meters on each side?

9. What is the area of a tablecloth needed to cover a tabletop that measures $2\frac{1}{3}$ feet on each side?

10. How much glass is needed to cover the front of a photograph that measures $3\frac{1}{2}$ inches on each side?

Finding the Volume of a Rectangular Solid

To find out how much space is *inside* things like boxes, suitcases, and rooms, you have to find volume. **Volume** is measured in cubic inches, cubic feet, cubic yards, and so on. To find the volume of things shaped like a rectangle, such as a shoebox, you multiply the length by the width by the height of the object. The formula is $V = lwh$. V stands for the volume, l stands for the length, w stands for the width, and h stands for the height.

EXAMPLE   Find the volume of a cardboard box that is 8 inches long, $4\frac{1}{2}$ inches wide, and $3\frac{1}{3}$ inches high.

$$8 \times 4\frac{1}{2} \times 3\frac{1}{3} = \frac{\overset{4}{\cancel{8}}}{1} \times \frac{\overset{3}{\cancel{9}}}{\underset{1}{\cancel{2}}} \times \frac{10}{\underset{1}{\cancel{3}}} = \textbf{120 cubic inches}$$

Solve each problem. Be sure to label each answer in cubic units.

1. Find the volume of a box that is 3 feet long, $2\frac{1}{2}$ feet wide, and $1\frac{1}{3}$ feet high.

2. Find the volume of a water tank that is 10 feet long, 8.5 feet wide, and 6.25 feet deep.

3. How many cubic feet of air are there in a room that is 12 feet long, 9 feet wide, and $8\frac{1}{2}$ feet high?

4. Find the volume of a briefcase that is 18 inches long, 12 inches wide, and $2\frac{3}{4}$ inches deep.

5. How much space is there inside a packing crate that is 16 inches long, $12\frac{1}{2}$ inches wide, and $7\frac{1}{2}$ inches high?

6. What is the volume of a matchbox that is 4 inches long, $2\frac{1}{2}$ inches wide, and $\frac{3}{4}$ inch high?

7. How many of the matchboxes in problem 6 fit inside the packing crate in problem 5?

8. What is the volume of a hole for a building foundation that is 20.4 meters long, 16.5 meters wide, and 3.8 meters deep?

9. How much concrete is in a sidewalk that is 63 feet long, 4 feet wide, and $\frac{1}{3}$ foot deep?

10. How much packing space is there in a trunk that is $4\frac{1}{3}$ feet long, $2\frac{1}{4}$ feet wide, and $2\frac{2}{3}$ feet high?

Finding the Circumference of a Circle

The distance across a circle is called the **diameter,** which can be shown by a straight line that goes through the center of a circle. The distance around a circle is called the **circumference.** To find the circumference of a circle, multiply the diameter of the circle by π (pi), a special number that has no exact value but is close to $\frac{22}{7}$ written as a fraction, or 3.14 written as a decimal.

The formula for the distance around a circle is $C = \pi d$. C is the circumference, π is $\frac{22}{7}$ or 3.14, and d is the diameter. Notice that π and d written next to each other means that they should be multiplied together.

EXAMPLE   Find the circumference of a circular chair seat with a diameter of 21 inches.

$$\frac{22}{7} \times 21 = \frac{22}{\cancel{7}_1} \times \frac{\cancel{21}^3}{1} = \textbf{66 inches}$$

Use π = $\frac{22}{7}$ to solve these problems.

1. Find the circumference of a circle with a diameter of 56 yards.

2. Mr. Casa wants to put a fence around a circular space in his backyard for his children to play in. If the space has a diameter of 35 feet, how many feet of fencing does he need?

3. If the fencing for problem 2 costs $2.15 a foot, how much will the fencing cost to enclose the space in Mr. Casa's backyard?

4. What is the circumference of a hubcap with a diameter of 10 inches?

5. Charles built a round table with a diameter of $3\frac{1}{2}$ feet. He wants to put metal stripping around the edge of the table. How many feet of stripping must he buy?

6. If the stripping for problem 5 costs $1.18 a foot, how much will Charles pay for the stripping to go around his table?

7. How many inches of wood are needed to make a frame for a circular mirror with a diameter of 28 inches?

8. How much fringe would be needed to trim a lampshade that has a diameter of 14 inches?

9. How much fencing is needed to go around a circular pool that has a diameter of 30 feet?

Finding the Area of a Circle

You already learned that the distance across a circle is called the diameter. The distance halfway across a circle is called the **radius.** The radius is $\frac{1}{2}$ the diameter. To find the area of a circle, multiply the radius by itself and then multiply this answer by π. The formula for finding the area of a circle is $A = \pi r^2$. A is the area, π is $\frac{22}{7}$ or 3.14, and r^2 is the radius multiplied by itself.

radius

EXAMPLE   Find the area of a circular hole in the floor with a radius of 2 inches.

$$\frac{22}{7} \times \frac{2}{1} \times \frac{2}{1} = \frac{88}{7} = 12\frac{4}{7} \text{ square inches}$$

Notice that the answer is in square units.

Use $\pi = \frac{22}{7}$ to solve these problems. Be sure to label each answer in square units.

1. Find the area of a circle with a radius of 7 feet.

2. If the radius of a circular pool is 10 feet, what is the area of the bottom of the pool?

3. Mrs. Twyman wants to cover the top of a round table with square tiles that are each 1-inch square. How many tiles will she need if the radius of her table is 14 inches?

4. Find the area of a circular play yard with a radius of 5 feet that Norman built for his dog.

5. If the tiles for the table in problem 3 cost $0.24 each, how much will Mrs. Twyman pay for the tiles to cover her table?

6. How large a bedspread is needed to cover a round bed with a radius of 2.1 meters?

7. How many square yards of dancing space are there on a round dance floor with a radius of $3\frac{1}{2}$ yards?

8. If flooring costs $45 per square yard, how much will the flooring cost to cover the dance floor?

9. Find the amount of space inside a circular garden with a radius of one foot.

10. A circular hole in Mr. Henry's wall has a radius of one-half foot. How much material does he need to cover it?

Changing a Recipe

Use the following list of ingredients needed for making a cake to answer the questions on this page.

1 cup of flour $1\frac{1}{3}$ cups of egg whites

$1\frac{1}{2}$ cups of sugar $1\frac{2}{3}$ teaspoons of cream of tartar

$\frac{1}{4}$ teaspoon of salt $1\frac{1}{4}$ teaspoons of vanilla

1. Fill in the amount of each ingredient you would need to make two cakes.

    _____ flour   _____ egg whites

    _____ sugar   _____ cream of tartar

    _____ salt   _____ vanilla

2. Fill in the amount of each ingredient you would need to make a smaller cake that is one-half the size of the cake in the recipe.

    _____ flour   _____ egg whites

    _____ sugar   _____ cream of tartar

    _____ salt   _____ vanilla

3. Fill in the amount of each ingredient you would need to make five cakes.

    _____ flour   _____ egg whites

    _____ sugar   _____ cream of tartar

    _____ salt   _____ vanilla

Converting Units of Measurement

In the United States we use a system of measurements called **standard** or **customary.** The system includes familiar units such as feet, pounds, and gallons. Much of the rest of the world uses the **metric system** in which the basic unit of length is the meter, the basic unit of weight is the kilogram, and the basic unit of liquid measure is the liter.

To convert from the standard system to the metric system, use the chart below.

To convert from	to	multiply by
miles (mi)	kilometers (km)	1.61
yards (yd)	meters (m)	0.91
feet (' or ft)	centimeters (cm)	30.48
inches (" or in.)	centimeters	2.54
square yards (sq yd)	square meters (sq m)	0.84
square feet (sq ft)	square meters	0.09
square inches (sq in.)	square centimeters (sq cm)	6.45
square miles (sq mi)	square kilometers (sq km)	2.59
pounds (lb)	kilograms (kg)	0.45
ounces (oz)	grams (g)	28.35
gallons (gal)	liters (l)	3.79
quarts (qt)	liters	0.95
pints (pt)	liters	0.47

EXAMPLE   Change 4 pounds to kilograms. Express the answer to the nearest *tenth*.

According to the chart, to change pounds to kilograms, multiply the number of pounds by 0.45. $4 \times 0.45 = \textbf{1.8}$

Use the table above to solve each problem. Use a calculator to check your answers.

1. The distance from Buffalo to Chicago is 540 miles. Find the distance in kilometers to the nearest *ten*.

2. The area of the Santiago's apartment is 750 square feet. To the nearest *unit*, what is the area of the apartment in square meters?

3. A 5-gallon jug of apple cider contains how many liters? Round to the nearest *unit*.

4. A typical sheet of typing paper measures 11 inches by $8\frac{1}{2}$ inches. Find each of these measurements to the nearest *tenth* of a centimeter.

5. Alfredo weighs 180 pounds. What is his weight in kilograms?

6. The area of Atlanta is 131 square miles. To the nearest *unit,* what is the area of Atlanta in square kilometers?

7. A letter weighs 1.2 ounces. Find the weight of the letter in grams to the nearest *unit*.

8. A bottle that contains $1\frac{1}{2}$ pints of cooking oil contains how many liters? Find the answer to the nearest *tenth*.

9. A 15-inch pipe is how long in centimeters? Find the answer to the nearest *unit*.

The table below tells how to convert from metric units to standard units.

To convert from	to	multiply by
kilometers	miles	0.62
meters	yards	1.09
meters	inches	39.37
meters	feet	3.28
centimeters	inches	0.39
square kilometers	square miles	0.39
square meters	square feet	10.76
kilograms	pounds	2.21
grams	ounces	0.04
liters	quarts	1.06
liters	gallons	0.26

Use the table on the previous page to solve these problems.

10. At birth little Max weighed 3.5 kilograms. What was his weight in pounds to the nearest *tenth*?

11. Pierre bought 38 liters of gasoline for his car. To the nearest *unit*, how many gallons of gasoline did he buy?

12. At the market Elena bought 0.6 kilogram of goat cheese. What was the weight of the cheese in pounds to the nearest *hundredth*?

13. The distance from New York to London is 5,539 kilometers. To the nearest *unit*, what is the distance between the cities in miles?

14. The average (or mean) distance from the earth to the moon is 384,000 kilometers. What is the distance to the nearest *thousand* miles?

15. The area of the kitchen floor in Amadou and Imani's house is 7.5 square meters. Find the area of their kitchen floor in square feet.

16. Sven's height is 1.85 meters. To the nearest *tenth*, what is his height in inches?

17. A bottle holds 1.5 liters of olive oil. To the nearest *tenth*, how many quarts does the bottle hold?

18. The area of Puerto Rico is 8,960 square kilometers. To the nearest *ten*, what is the area of the island in square miles?

19. Find the weight in ounces of 60 grams of salt.

20. The area of the ground floor in the Diallo family's house is 100 square meters. What is the area of the ground floor in square feet?

Finding Interest for One Year

Interest is money that money earns. On a loan, **interest** is the payment you must make for using the lender's money. On a savings account, interest is the money the bank pays you for using your money.

The formula for finding interest is $i = prt$.

i is the *interest* in dollars.

p is the *principal*, the money borrowed or saved.

r is the percent *rate*, which can be written as either a fraction or a decimal.

t is the *time* in years.

The formula is read as *interest is equal to the principal times the rate times the time.*

EXAMPLE 1 Find the interest on $500 at 8% annual interest for one year.

$$\overset{5}{\cancel{500}} \times \frac{8}{\underset{1}{\cancel{100}}} \times 1 = \textbf{\$40}$$

Notice that the percent was changed to a fraction with a denominator of 100.

EXAMPLE 2 Find the interest on $600 at $4\frac{1}{2}$% annual interest for one year.

$$\frac{\overset{300}{\cancel{600}}}{100} \times \frac{9}{\underset{1}{\cancel{2}}} \times 1 = \frac{2700}{100} = \textbf{\$27}$$

Change $4\frac{1}{2}$% to an improper fraction ($\frac{9}{2}$) and put a denominator of 100 under the principal.

EXAMPLE 3 Find the interest on $400 at 8.5% for one year.

$$
\begin{array}{r}
\$400 \\
\times\, 0.085 \\
\hline
2\,000 \\
32\,00 \\
\hline
34.00\cancel{0} \\
\times\quad 1 \\
\hline
\textbf{\$34.00}
\end{array}
$$

Write 8.5% as a decimal (0.085).

Solve each problem.

1. Manny borrowed $800 at 10% annual interest. How much interest did he owe in one year?

2. Deborah borrowed $450 at 15% annual interest. How much interest did she owe in one year?

3. Frank put $200 in his savings account for one year. If his money earned $2\frac{1}{2}$% annual interest, how much interest did he get in a year?

4. Diane borrowed $1,000 in order to finish a year in school. If she had to pay 6.7% interest on the loan, how much interest did she owe after one year?

5. Ellen saved $600 for a year. How much interest did she earn if her bank pays an annual interest rate of $2\frac{1}{4}$%?

6. How much interest did Daniel owe on a $1,500 loan in one year if his bank charged him 11.5% interest?

7. José had to pay 8.4% interest on a $950 loan. How much interest did he owe in one year?

8. Madge kept $1,200 in a certificate of deposit (CD) for a year. How much interest did she earn if her CD paid $4\frac{3}{4}$% annual interest?

Finding Interest for Less than One Year

Interest rates are usually given for one year. If you want to find interest for less than one year, write the number of months over 12 (the number of months in one year). Use this fraction for t in the formula $i = prt$.

EXAMPLE   Find the interest on $500 at 8% annual interest for nine months.

STEP 1   9 months $= \dfrac{9 \text{ months}}{12 \text{ months per year}} = \dfrac{3}{4}$ year

STEP 2 $\dfrac{\overset{5}{\cancel{500}}}{1} \times \dfrac{\overset{2}{\cancel{8}}}{\underset{1}{\cancel{100}}} \times \dfrac{3}{\underset{1}{\cancel{4}}} = 30

Solve each problem.

1. Find the interest on $900 at 6% annual interest for four months.

2. Mary's bank pays 2.5% annual interest on savings accounts. How much interest will Mary make on $1,000 in six months?

3. David's charge account costs him 18% in annual interest. How much interest would he owe on $700 in 10 months?

4. Jane kept $270 in her savings account for 8 months. How much interest will she get if her bank pays 2% annual interest?

5. Fred was charged 9.2% annual interest on a $1,200 loan. How much interest did he owe if he paid the loan back in two months?

Finding Interest for More than One Year

If you want to find interest for more than one year, write the total number of months over 12 (the number of months in one year). Use this improper fraction for *t* in the formula *i = prt*.

EXAMPLE   Find the interest on $600 at 5% annual interest for one year and 6 months.

STEP 1   1 year and 6 months = $\dfrac{18 \text{ months}}{12 \text{ months per year}} = \dfrac{3}{2}$ years

STEP 2 $\dfrac{\cancel{600}^{3}}{1} \times \dfrac{5}{\cancel{100}_{1}} \times \dfrac{3}{\cancel{2}_{1}} = \$45$

Solve each problem.

1. Find the interest on $800 at 9% annual interest for two years and three months.

2. Carlos borrowed $1,500 at 11% annual interest. He paid the loan back in one year and eight months. How much interest did he pay?

3. Sally kept $400 in her bank account for one year and nine months. How much interest did she make if her bank pays $2\frac{1}{2}$% annual interest?

4. Mr. Clay paid back his $2,000 car loan two years and six months after he borrowed the money. If he was charged 10.5% annual interest, how much interest did he pay?

5. Jack's bank pays $2\frac{1}{4}$% annual interest on Jack's account. How much interest will Jack make on a $600 deposit that he keeps in the bank for one year and four months?

Finding Compound Interest

In most savings accounts, money earns **compound interest.** This means that your balance (the principal) changes by the addition of interest on a regular time basis such as quarterly (every three months), monthly, or even daily.

EXAMPLE Joe deposited $500 in his savings account. How much money will he have in the account at the end of a year if he gets 4% annual interest and the interest is **compounded** (added to his balance) quarterly.

STEP 1 First quarter: $\dfrac{\overset{5}{\cancel{500}}}{1} \times \dfrac{\overset{1}{\cancel{4}}}{\underset{1}{\cancel{100}}} \times \dfrac{1}{\underset{1}{\cancel{4}}} = \$5.00$

Amount in account: $500 + $5 = **$505.00**

STEP 2 Second quarter: Joe gets interest on the new balance, $505.00.

$\dfrac{\overset{101}{\cancel{505}}}{1} \times \dfrac{\overset{1}{\cancel{4}}}{\underset{20}{\cancel{100}}} \times \dfrac{1}{\underset{1}{\cancel{4}}} = \dfrac{101}{20} = \$5.05$

Amount in account: $505 + $5.05 = **$510.05**

STEP 3 Third quarter: The interest is calculated on $510.05.

$\dfrac{\overset{102.01}{\cancel{510.05}}}{1} \times \dfrac{\overset{1}{\cancel{4}}}{\underset{20}{\cancel{100}}} \times \dfrac{1}{\underset{1}{\cancel{4}}} = \dfrac{102.01}{20} = \$5.10$ (rounded to the nearest cent)

Amount in account: $510.05 + $5.10 = **$515.15**

STEP 4 Fourth quarter: The interest is calculated on $515.15.

$\dfrac{\overset{103.03}{\cancel{515.15}}}{1} \times \dfrac{\overset{1}{\cancel{4}}}{\underset{20}{\cancel{100}}} \times \dfrac{1}{\underset{1}{\cancel{4}}} = \dfrac{103.03}{20} = \$5.15$ (rounded to the nearest cent)

Amount in account: $515.15 + $5.15 = **$520.30**

Notice that every quarter the new principal was used to calculate the amount of interest.

Solve each problem. Round answers to the nearest cent.

Luis put $800 in his savings account which pays 6% annual interest.
How much will he have in his account in a year if the interest is
compounded quarterly?

1. **a.** first quarter interest   **b.** first quarter principal

2. **a.** second quarter interest   **b.** second quarter principal

3. **a.** third quarter interest   **b.** third quarter principal

4. **a.** fourth quarter interest   **b.** fourth quarter principal

Denise kept $1,200 in a savings account that pays 8% annual interest.
How much will she have in her account in a year if the interest is
compounded quarterly?

5. **a.** first quarter interest   **b.** first quarter principal

6. **a.** second quarter interest   **b.** second quarter principal

7. **a.** third quarter interest   **b.** third quarter principal

8. **a.** fourth quarter interest   **b.** fourth quarter principal

To cover college expenses Jake borrowed $20,000 from his older brother
Jed. They agreed that Jake would pay a low 5% interest, compounded
annually for four years. How much will Jake owe his brother at the end
of four years?

9. **a.** first year interest   **b.** first year principal

10. **a.** second year interest   **b.** second year principal

11. **a.** third year interest   **b.** third year principal

12. **a.** fourth year interest   **b.** fourth year principal

Comparing Food Prices: Unit Pricing

Similar food items come in different package sizes. It is not always easy to tell which package is the best buy. Suppose you find two different brands of peas, one in a 16-ounce can priced at 72¢ and another in a 10-ounce can priced at 55¢. To find the best buy, calculate the price per ounce of peas in each can. The word *per* suggests division. Finding this price is called **unit pricing.**

EXAMPLE   Which of these two brands of peas is cheaper?

16-ounce can of Brand X peas for 72¢

10-ounce can of Brand Y peas for 55¢

The cost per ounce for Brand X is

$$16\overline{)72} = 4\frac{8}{16} = 4\frac{1}{2} \text{¢ per ounce}$$
$$\underline{64}$$
$$8$$

The cost per ounce for Brand Y is

$$10\overline{)55} = 5\frac{5}{10} = 5\frac{1}{2} \text{¢ per ounce}$$
$$\underline{50}$$
$$5$$

ANSWER: Brand X is cheaper.

Use the advertising posters below to answer the questions on the next page. For quick comparisons, use a calculator.

FRED'S FOODS

Margarine   2 8-oz cups $1.79

48 size, Indian River
seedless grapefruit   7 for $2

orange juice

1/2-gallon cont. $2.09

GERT'S GROCERIES

Margarine   3 8-oz cups $2.49

INDIAN RIVER SEEDLESS
GRAPEFRUIT
(48 SIZE)

6 FOR $1.78

Orange Juice   64-OZ BTL. $1.99

SAM'S STORE

Margarine
1-lb pkg. $1.59

FLORIDA SEEDLESS
Grapefruit   4 for 98¢

Orange Juice

3 1-qt conts. $3.15

1. What was the price of 8 ounces of margarine

    a. at Fred's Foods?

    b. at Gert's Groceries?

    c. at Sam's Store? (1 pound = 16 ounces)

    d. Which store had the least expensive margarine?

2. What was the price of one seedless grapefruit

    a. at Fred's Foods?

    b. at Gert's Groceries?

    c. at Sam's Store?

    d. Which store had the least expensive grapefruit?

3. What was the price of one quart (32 ounces) of orange juice

    a. at Fred's Foods?

    b. at Gert's Groceries?

    c. at Sam's Store?

    d. Which store had the least expensive orange juice?

Finding the Percent Saved at a Sale

To find what percent you save by buying an item on sale, put the amount saved over the original price, reduce, and change the fraction into a percent.

EXAMPLE **All the prints that fit . . . on sale!** Long-sleeved boys' shirts in assorted prints. 100% cotton, sizes S-M-L.
reg. $15 . . . . **sale $10**

What percent of the original price can you save by buying the shirt on sale?

STEP 1 The regular price is $15. The sale price is $10. The amount saved is $15 − $10 = $5.

STEP 2 $\dfrac{\text{savings}}{\text{original}} = \dfrac{\$5}{\$15} = \dfrac{1}{3} = 33\dfrac{1}{3}\%$

Find the percent of savings for each item shown in this advertisement.

STARR'S DISCOUNT STORE

Let Us Make You a Starr!

Gigantic Savings—Storewide Clearance Sale

Wizard® canister vacuum. 2.3 hp (peak-rated by manufacturer); automatic cord rewind; tools, more! Add $2 delivery.
orig. $100 . . . . **sale $62**

Men's sleeveless print sport shirts. Splashy patterns, geometrics; assorted colors. Cotton, polyester/cotton or nylon. S-M-L-XL.
orig. $15 . . . . **sale $8**

Fashion's most popular pre-washed denim fabric. 45" wide.
reg. $6 . . . . **sale $3 yd**

Girls' pants. Daisy print. Sizes 8, 10, 12, 14, 16.
orig. $18 . . . . **sale $9**

Men's hooded fleece jackets. Zip or button-front. S-M-L-XL.
reg. $35 . . . . **sale $20**

Men's cotton shorts. Sizes 32-40.
reg. $18 . . . . **sale $14**

Misses' cotton crewneck T-shirt for skirts or jeans! Stripe combinations of blue, green, brown. S-M-L.
reg. $11 . . . . **sale $8**

Boys' canvas slip-on shoes. Assorted colors; rubber sole. Sizes 1-11.
reg. $7.50 . . . . **sale $6**

Men's nylon warm-up suits. Buy separates or set. Blue or bone. Team name on jacket. Sizes S-M-L-XL.
reg. $27 each . . . **sale $19 each**

Geometric-design blankets. 100% acrylic; machine wash, tumble dry. Brown/blue reverses to solid blue.
Twin, orig. $25 . . . . . . **sale $19**

Full, orig. $35 . . . . . . **sale $29**

1. Wizard canister vacuum

2. Pre-washed denim fabric

3. Men's hooded fleece jacket

4. Misses' cotton T-shirt

5. Men's nylon warm-up suit

6. Men's sleeveless sport shirt

7. Girls' pants

8. Men's cotton shorts

9. Boys' canvas shoes

10. Twin-size blanket

11. Full-size blanket

Buying Furniture on Sale

When Deborah Robinson went into the Friendly Furniture Store, she saw these signs.

Every Lamp 25% Off	All Baby Furniture $33\frac{1}{3}$% Off

Deborah decided to buy a pair of lamps that had originally sold for $78.00 each and a high chair that originally cost $49.95.

Use the information above to answer the following questions.

1. How much money could she save on each lamp?

2. What was the sale price of each lamp?

3. How much money could she save on the high chair?

4. What was the sale price of the high chair?

5. What was the total price for the two lamps and the high chair?

6. In Deborah's state there is an 8% sales tax. How much did she owe for her furniture including tax?

7. On February 4, Deborah deposited her paycheck of $535.70 and $30.00 in cash in her checking account. Fill out the deposit slip on the next page as she would.

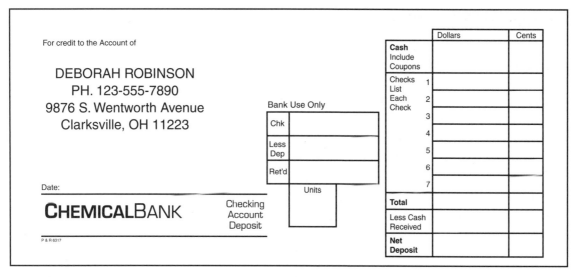

8. On February 6, Deborah went back to the store and paid for the lamps and the high chair with a check. Fill out the check below as she would and enter the check and deposit on the form that follows.

DEBORAH ROBINSON
PH. 123-555-7890
9876 S. Wentworth Avenue
Clarksville, OH 11223

No. 004

_____ 20 __ $\frac{1\text{-}12}{210}$

PAY TO THE ORDER OF _____ $ _____

_____ DOLLARS

CHEMICALBANK

FOR _____ _____

CHECK NO.	DATE	CHECK ISSUED TO	AMOUNT OF CHECK		√ T	FEE (IF ANY)	AMOUNT OF DEPOSIT		BALANCE	
									585	00
001	1/21	Telephone Company	35	70					549	30
002	1/29	Utility Company	15	36					533	94
003	2/1	Rental Agent	345	00					188	94
	2/4	Deposit					565	70	754	64
004										

Using a Tax Rate Schedule

An important part of filling out income tax forms is using a tax rate schedule. Tax rate schedules let you know how much money you have to pay in taxes based on how much money you made during the year. The tax rate schedule on this page is for heads of household. The **head of household** is the person who brings in the money or most of the money on which a family lives.

This schedule is used to figure out the amount of money owed to the federal government. The amount is based on the taxable income entered on line 37 of tax form 1040. Both tax rate schedules and tax forms can be obtained from the Internal Revenue Service.

Schedule Z—Use if your filing status is **Head of household**

If the amount on Form 1040, line 37, is: Over—	But not over—	Enter on Form 1040, line 38		of the amount over—
$0	$29,600	----------	15%	$0
29,600	76,400	$4,440.00 +	28%	29,600
76,400	127,500	17,544.00 +	31%	76,400
127,500	250,000	33,385.00 +	36%	127,500
250,000	-------	77,485.00 +	39.6%	250,000

EXAMPLE   What amount goes on line 38 of form 1040 if the amount on line 37 is $31,000?

STEP 1   Read the tax rate schedule from left to right. Since $31,000 is between $29,600 and $76,400, the amount for line 38 is $4,440 plus 28% of the excess (additional dollars) over $29,600.

STEP 2   Find the excess over $29,600.

$$\begin{array}{r} \$31,000 \\ -\ 29,600 \\ \hline 1,400 \end{array}$$

STEP 3   Find 28% of $1,400.

$$\begin{array}{r} \$1,400 \\ \times\ .28 \\ \hline 112\ 00 \\ 280\ 0 \\ \hline 392.00 \end{array}$$

STEP 4   Add.
$$\begin{array}{r} \$4,440 \\ +\ 392 \\ \hline \$4,832\ \text{tax owed} \end{array}$$

Use the schedule on page 162 to find the following.

1. If line 37 is $42,600, what will be the amount on line 38?

2. If line 37 is $29,900, what will be the amount on line 38?

3. If line 37 is $81,900, what will be the amount on line 38?

4. If line 37 is $21,500, what will be the amount on line 38?

5. If line 37 is $50,313, what will be the amount on line 38?

6. If line 37 is $130,100, what will be the amount on line 38?

7. If line 37 is $77,246, what will be the amount on line 38?

8. If line 37 is $96,412, what will be the amount on line 38?

9. If line 37 is $68,300, what will be the amount on line 38?

10. If line 37 is $15,555, what will be the amount on line 38?

Filling Out a Wage and Tax Statement

Peter Cheung made a gross salary (before deductions) of $23,650 in 1999 at Colver Products in New York. His employers withheld (deducted) from his gross pay certain amounts for federal income tax, state income tax, city income tax, and FICA (social security).

1. 14.2% of Mr. Cheung's gross annual salary of $23,650 was withheld for federal income tax. How much money was withheld from his pay for federal tax?

2. 5.8% of Mr. Cheung's gross salary was withheld for FICA. How much money was withheld for FICA?

3. 4.1% of Mr. Cheung's gross salary was withheld for state income tax. How much money was withheld for state tax?

4. 1.4% of Mr. Cheung's gross salary was withheld for city income tax. How much was withheld for city tax?

5. An additional $300 was taken out for Medicare tax. What was Mr. Cheung's net (take-home) pay for 1999?

6. Finish completing the Wage and Tax Statement on the next page. Put Mr. Cheung's gross pay in boxes 1, 3, 5, 17, and 20. Put the federal income tax withheld in box 2. Put the FICA withheld in box 4. Put the state tax withheld in box 18. Put the city tax withheld in box 21.

OMB No 1545-0008		
a Control number	**1** Wages, tips, other compensation	**2** Federal income tax withheld
	3 Social security wages	**4** Social security tax withheld
	5 Medicare wages and tips	**6** Medicare tax withheld $300

c Employer's name, address, and ZIP code

Colver Products
333 East 49th Street
New York, N.Y. 10017

7 Social security tips *None*	**8** Allocated tips *None*	**9** Advance EIC payment *None*
10 Dependent care benefits *None*	**11** Nonqualified plans *None*	**12** Benefits included in Box 1 *None*

b Employer's identification number *13-5009-340*	**d** Employee's social security number *123-45-6789*
13 See Instrs. for Box 13	**14** Other *None*

e Employee's name, address, and ZIP code

Peter Cheung
5 East Third Street
New York, N.Y. 10003

15 Statutory employee	Deceased	Pension plan X	Legal rep	942 emp	Subtotal	Deferred compensasion

1999	**16** State *N.Y.* Employer's state I.D. No. *21-4952*	**17** State wages, tips,etc.
Form **W-2** Wage and Tax Statement copy For **EMPLOYEE'S** State, City, or Local Income Tax Return	**18** State income tax	**19** Locality name *New York*
	20 Local wages, tips, etc.	**21** Local income tax

Department of the Treasury—Internal Revenue Service

7. Use the tax rate schedule on page 162 to find out how much federal income tax Mr. Cheung owed. Write his check below to the Internal Revenue Service dated April 15, 1999, for the balance that he owed.

PETER CHEUNG
5 East Third Street
New York, NY 10003

No. 021

_____ 19 ___ $\frac{1\text{-}12}{210}$

PAY TO THE ORDER OF _____ $ _____

_____ DOLLARS

CHEMICALBANK

FOR _____ _____

Working with a Budget

The budget below shows the way that the four members of the Johnson family spend their money.

1. The income for the Johnson family comes from Mr. Johnson's yearly salary of $50,000. 28% of his salary is withheld for taxes and social security. How much money is withheld for taxes and social security in a year?

2. What is Mr. Johnson's yearly take-home pay?

Use the budget below and Mr. Johnson's take-home pay to fill in the amount budgeted for each expense.

Johnson Family Yearly Budget		
Expenses	**% Budgeted**	**Amount Budgeted**
Rent	20%	
Food	31%	
Utilities	5%	
Entertainment	6%	
Clothes	10%	
Medical	12%	
Savings	10%	
Odds and Ends	6%	

Buying on an Installment Plan

Buying on an installment plan is a way to make partial payments for an item. However, by paying in regular installments, a customer can end up paying much more than the list price of an item. The problems that follow show how different cash prices and installment prices can be.

For each problem, use the given information to answer the questions.

1. A lawn mower marked $159 can be bought for 10% down and $15 a week for 12 weeks.

   a. What is the cash price of the lawn mower including 8% sales tax?

   b. How much does the lawn mower cost on the installment plan?

   c. How much more does it cost to buy the lawn mower on the installment plan than it does to pay cash?

2. An upright vacuum cleaner is priced at $89. It can be bought for no payment down and $11 a month for 1 year.

   a. What is the cash price of the vacuum cleaner including 7% sales tax?

   b. How much does the vacuum cleaner cost on the installment plan?

   c. How much more does it cost to buy the vacuum cleaner on the installment plan than it does to pay cash?

3. A kitchen table and chair set marked $395 can be bought for 15% down and $35 a month for 1 year.

   a. What is the cash price of the furniture including 6% sales tax?

   b. How much does the furniture cost on the installment plan?

   c. How much more does it cost to buy the furniture on the installment plan than it does to pay cash?

4. A color television marked $459.00 can be bought for 8% down and $10.50 a week for 1 year.

   a. What is the cash price of the television including 5% sales tax?

   b. How much does the television cost on the installment plan?

   c. How much more does it cost to buy the television on the installment plan than it does to pay cash?

5. A mattress and box-spring set is priced at $289.95. They can be bought for 12% down and $14.80 a week for 22 weeks.

   a. What is the cash price of the mattress and box-spring set including 6% sales tax?

   b. How much does the mattress and box-spring set cost on the installment plan?

   c. How much more does it cost to buy the mattress and box-spring set on the installment plan than it does to pay cash?

6. An air conditioner marked $229 can be bought for 16% down and $25 per month for 1 year.

   a. What is the cash price of the air conditioner including 5% sales tax?

   b. How much does the air conditioner cost on the installment plan?

   c. How much more does it cost to buy the air conditioner on the installment plan than it does to pay cash?

Answer Key

Pages 1–5, Pretest

1. $\frac{3}{4}$
2. $8\frac{23}{24}$
3. greater than 1
4. $36\frac{1}{8}$ inches
5. $4\frac{19}{30}$
6. $2\frac{13}{16}$ pounds
7. $\frac{5}{18}$
8. 35
9. 15
10. 16 students
11. $\frac{1}{2}$
12. $2\frac{8}{9}$
13. $3\frac{1}{2}$ inches
14. 48 words
15. 12.016
16. 0.057, 0.075, 0.57, 0.7
17. 18.708
18. 1.625 inches
19. 1.703
20. 6.8
21. 17.6 square miles
22. 10.582
23. 72
24. $9.57
25. 3.8
26. 200
27. 12.6
28. 42.9 pounds
29. 0.048
30. $41\frac{2}{3}\%$
31. $\frac{1}{16}$
32. 81
33. 6
34. d. $75 \div 5$
35. 14 items
36. 2,760 people
37. 75%
38. $62\frac{1}{2}\%$
39. 80%
40. 60%
41. 120
42. 130 seats
43. 48 streets

Pages 8–10, Fraction Skills Inventory

1. $\frac{5}{8}$
2. $\frac{5}{6}$, $\frac{3}{4}$
3. $\frac{2}{3}$
4. $2\frac{2}{5}$
5. $\frac{38}{7}$
6. $\frac{12}{18}$
7. $8\frac{1}{5}$
8. $11\frac{11}{12}$
9. less than 1
10. $26\frac{13}{16}$ pounds
11. $6\frac{1}{4}$ hours
12. $6\frac{7}{20}$
13. $4\frac{1}{2}$
14. $3\frac{13}{21}$
15. $124\frac{1}{2}$ pounds
16. $27\frac{1}{2}$ inches
17. $\frac{21}{40}$
18. $\frac{1}{4}$
19. 15
20. $2 \times 3 = 6$

21. 28 crates
22. $37\frac{1}{2}$ hours
23. $1\frac{1}{9}$
24. 16
25. $\frac{1}{18}$
26. $2\frac{3}{16}$
27. 48
28. 28 bags
29. 10 pieces

Page 11

1. $\frac{1}{6}$
2. $\frac{5}{8}$
3. $\frac{3}{4}$
4. $\frac{3}{8}$
5. $\frac{2}{5}$
6. $\frac{4}{9}$
7. $\frac{5}{6}$
8. $\frac{2}{3}$
9. $\frac{5}{9}$

Page 12

1. $\frac{5}{12}$
2. $\frac{47}{100}$
3. $\frac{9}{16}$
4. $\frac{23}{36}$
5. $\frac{7}{12}$
6. $\frac{8}{25}$
7. $\frac{43}{60}$
8. $\frac{1,351}{2,000}$
9. $\frac{2}{5}$
10. $\frac{63}{100}$
11. $\frac{3}{4}$
12. $\frac{113}{350}$
13. $\frac{77}{280}$

Page 13

1. I P M I
2. P I I M
3. M P P I
4. P I M P

Page 14

1. $\frac{6}{12}, \frac{9}{18}, \frac{8}{16}, \frac{12}{24}$
2. $\frac{2}{7}, \frac{3}{8}, \frac{4}{9}, \frac{9}{20}, \frac{4}{15}$
3. $\frac{3}{4}, \frac{7}{8}, \frac{9}{15}, \frac{8}{12}, \frac{17}{30}$
4. $> \frac{1}{2}$ $= \frac{1}{2}$ $< \frac{1}{2}$ $> \frac{1}{2}$

Pages 16–17

1. $\frac{1}{2}$ $\frac{1}{4}$ $\frac{1}{3}$ $\frac{1}{5}$ $\frac{1}{8}$
2. $\frac{5}{6}$ $\frac{8}{9}$ $\frac{8}{9}$ $\frac{7}{8}$ $\frac{2}{3}$
3. $\frac{2}{5}$ $\frac{1}{3}$ $\frac{7}{20}$ $\frac{9}{14}$ $\frac{8}{17}$
4. $\frac{3}{7}$ $\frac{3}{4}$ $\frac{1}{2}$ $\frac{3}{4}$ $\frac{3}{4}$
5. $\frac{15}{16}$ $\frac{7}{8}$ $\frac{4}{9}$ $\frac{2}{3}$ $\frac{9}{16}$
6. $\frac{1}{2}$ $\frac{1}{3}$ $\frac{1}{50}$ $\frac{7}{9}$ $\frac{5}{7}$

7. $\frac{2}{3}$ 12. $\frac{2}{3}$ 17. $\frac{5}{9}$

8. $\frac{3}{5}$ 13. $\frac{1}{3}$ 18. $\frac{4}{9}$

9. $\frac{2}{5}$ 14. $\frac{1}{4}$ 19. $\frac{5}{8}$

10. $\frac{1}{10}$ 15. $\frac{3}{4}$ 20. $\frac{3}{8}$

11. $\frac{5}{8}$ 16. $\frac{1}{8}$

Page 18

1. $\frac{24}{30}$ $\frac{18}{20}$ $\frac{3}{18}$ $\frac{20}{32}$

2. $\frac{20}{35}$ $\frac{18}{36}$ $\frac{14}{21}$ $\frac{54}{66}$

3. $\frac{25}{45}$ $\frac{33}{44}$ $\frac{35}{60}$ $\frac{15}{45}$

4. $\frac{25}{50}$ $\frac{15}{40}$ $\frac{16}{72}$ $\frac{35}{42}$

Page 20

1. $1\frac{3}{4}$ $5\frac{1}{2}$ $2\frac{4}{5}$ $4\frac{2}{7}$ 4

2. $3\frac{1}{3}$ $3\frac{1}{4}$ 3 $3\frac{3}{5}$ 2

3. $1\frac{1}{12}$ 5 $7\frac{1}{2}$ $2\frac{2}{3}$ $4\frac{2}{3}$

4. 3 $2\frac{4}{5}$ $5\frac{1}{2}$ $2\frac{3}{4}$ $12\frac{1}{2}$

5. $1\frac{2}{3}$

6. $2\frac{2}{3}$

7. $1\frac{1}{4}$

8. $8\frac{1}{2}$

Page 21

1. $\frac{11}{4}$ $\frac{11}{7}$ $\frac{16}{3}$ $\frac{44}{7}$ $\frac{23}{5}$

2. $\frac{19}{2}$ $\frac{61}{8}$ $\frac{29}{10}$ $\frac{35}{4}$ $\frac{32}{9}$

3. $\frac{31}{3}$ $\frac{57}{5}$ $\frac{53}{12}$ $\frac{55}{8}$ $\frac{49}{4}$

4. $\frac{19}{5}$ $\frac{43}{7}$ $\frac{75}{8}$ $\frac{25}{12}$ $\frac{79}{15}$

Pages 22–24

1. $\frac{5}{9}$ $\frac{4}{7}$ $\frac{7}{8}$ $\frac{7}{12}$ $\frac{10}{13}$

2. $\frac{6}{11}$ $\frac{8}{9}$ $\frac{13}{15}$ $\frac{15}{17}$ $\frac{16}{19}$

3. $7\frac{3}{5}$ $14\frac{9}{10}$ $9\frac{9}{11}$ $14\frac{11}{13}$

4. $12\frac{8}{9}$ $17\frac{9}{11}$ $20\frac{6}{7}$ $15\frac{9}{10}$

5. $\frac{3}{4}$ $\frac{2}{3}$ $\frac{2}{3}$ $\frac{2}{3}$ $\frac{1}{2}$

6. $\frac{4}{5}$ $\frac{4}{5}$ $\frac{7}{10}$ $\frac{3}{4}$ $\frac{2}{3}$

7. $11\frac{1}{2}$ $16\frac{2}{3}$ $18\frac{6}{7}$ $42\frac{2}{3}$

8. $24\frac{2}{3}$ $17\frac{4}{5}$ $17\frac{3}{4}$ $31\frac{3}{4}$

9. $1\frac{2}{5}$ $1\frac{3}{8}$ $1\frac{3}{10}$ $1\frac{4}{9}$ 1

10. $1\frac{1}{3}$ $1\frac{1}{7}$ $1\frac{1}{2}$ $1\frac{1}{5}$ $1\frac{1}{2}$

11. $2\frac{2}{9}$ 2 $1\frac{1}{2}$ $2\frac{1}{4}$ $2\frac{1}{4}$

12. $17\frac{7}{8}$ $18\frac{2}{3}$ $18\frac{1}{10}$ 18

Page 25

1. $1\frac{1}{4}$ $1\frac{1}{2}$ $1\frac{5}{8}$ $1\frac{1}{6}$ $1\frac{2}{9}$

2. $1\frac{5}{8}$ $1\frac{1}{3}$ $1\frac{4}{5}$ $1\frac{1}{3}$ $1\frac{1}{5}$

3. $1\frac{2}{5}$ 2 $\frac{11}{12}$ $1\frac{2}{3}$ $1\frac{2}{5}$

Pages 26–28

1. $1\frac{4}{15}$ $1\frac{1}{12}$ $\frac{9}{10}$ $\frac{16}{21}$ $1\frac{7}{30}$

2. $1\frac{9}{28}$ $1\frac{5}{42}$ $1\frac{7}{40}$ $1\frac{1}{33}$ $1\frac{7}{45}$

3. $1\frac{7}{12}$ $1\frac{5}{18}$ $1\frac{9}{20}$ $\frac{35}{36}$ $1\frac{5}{24}$

4. $2\frac{1}{24}$ $1\frac{11}{20}$ $2\frac{17}{36}$ $1\frac{7}{16}$ $1\frac{5}{9}$

5. $1\frac{1}{2}$ $1\frac{23}{24}$ $1\frac{3}{4}$ $1\frac{1}{40}$ $1\frac{1}{36}$

6. $1\frac{17}{18}$ $2\frac{3}{28}$ $\frac{13}{18}$ $1\frac{52}{63}$ $1\frac{43}{48}$

7. $11\frac{7}{20}$ $17\frac{7}{24}$ $12\frac{2}{9}$

8. $13\frac{19}{24}$ $18\frac{13}{21}$ $10\frac{11}{12}$

9. $16\frac{3}{20}$ $16\frac{5}{18}$ $13\frac{5}{24}$

10. $11\frac{1}{18}$ $15\frac{19}{40}$ $12\frac{17}{30}$

11. $17\frac{29}{30}$ $19\frac{7}{24}$ $17\frac{29}{36}$

12. $22\frac{1}{12}$ $13\frac{1}{24}$ $21\frac{19}{36}$

13. $15\frac{9}{16}$ $23\frac{1}{4}$ $15\frac{11}{12}$

14. $24\frac{11}{70}$ $24\frac{11}{18}$ $17\frac{45}{56}$

Page 29

1. <1 $=1$ >1 $=1$

2. <1 >1 >1 <1

3. 4 and 5   7. 8 and 9

4. 9 and 10   8. 7 and 8

5. 11 and 12   9. 6 and 7

6. 6 and 7   10. 16 and 17

Exact answers are given below.

1. $\frac{13}{16}$ 1 $1\frac{2}{5}$ 1

2. $\frac{7}{8}$ $1\frac{1}{2}$ $1\frac{17}{30}$ $\frac{59}{72}$

3. $4\frac{1}{4}$ 7. $8\frac{31}{40}$

4. $9\frac{11}{24}$ 8. $7\frac{2}{3}$

5. $11\frac{1}{2}$ 9. $6\frac{47}{90}$

6. $6\frac{4}{5}$ 10. $16\frac{3}{14}$

Page 30

1. $68\frac{1}{4}$ inches
2. $16\frac{1}{10}$ miles
3. $22\frac{7}{20}$ pounds
4. $8\frac{19}{24}$ pounds
5. $14\frac{1}{4}$ hours
6. $128\frac{7}{10}$ pounds
7. $2\frac{23}{30}$ hours

Page 31

1. $\frac{1}{3}$ $\frac{1}{10}$ $\frac{1}{2}$ $\frac{3}{13}$ $\frac{6}{11}$
2. $\frac{1}{3}$ $\frac{3}{8}$ $\frac{1}{2}$ $\frac{3}{19}$ $\frac{1}{5}$
3. $3\frac{4}{7}$ 6 $1\frac{1}{3}$ $4\frac{2}{5}$
4. $8\frac{1}{4}$ $9\frac{1}{2}$ $9\frac{5}{13}$ $16\frac{2}{3}$

Pages 32–33

1. $\frac{1}{4}$ $\frac{3}{8}$ $\frac{1}{2}$ $\frac{9}{16}$ $\frac{1}{5}$
2. $\frac{5}{12}$ $\frac{7}{15}$ $\frac{13}{28}$ $\frac{7}{30}$ $\frac{7}{18}$
3. $6\frac{13}{24}$ $6\frac{3}{14}$ $7\frac{26}{45}$ $3\frac{1}{20}$
4. $6\frac{11}{56}$ $15\frac{23}{36}$ $7\frac{13}{30}$ $12\frac{5}{33}$
5. $5\frac{1}{4}$ $3\frac{3}{8}$ $2\frac{2}{21}$
6. $2\frac{5}{16}$ $9\frac{1}{5}$ $5\frac{14}{45}$
7. $1\frac{1}{28}$ $7\frac{7}{30}$ $7\frac{7}{24}$
8. $4\frac{1}{12}$ $7\frac{17}{56}$ $7\frac{11}{63}$
9. $1\frac{23}{72}$ $4\frac{17}{42}$ $2\frac{11}{24}$
10. $6\frac{5}{24}$ $3\frac{1}{30}$ $2\frac{7}{20}$
11. $8\frac{1}{12}$ $8\frac{1}{30}$ $4\frac{1}{14}$
12. $2\frac{5}{24}$ $7\frac{2}{15}$ $9\frac{3}{10}$
13. $6\frac{1}{6}$ $4\frac{1}{10}$ $11\frac{13}{84}$
14. $3\frac{7}{30}$ $5\frac{1}{9}$ $3\frac{9}{40}$

Pages 35–36

1. $7\frac{1}{6}$ $3\frac{4}{7}$ $11\frac{1}{2}$ $8\frac{3}{5}$ $9\frac{3}{11}$
2. $3\frac{4}{7}$ $3\frac{1}{3}$ $1\frac{5}{12}$ $3\frac{4}{9}$ $6\frac{11}{16}$
3. $3\frac{2}{3}$ $6\frac{1}{2}$ $7\frac{2}{3}$ $6\frac{2}{5}$
4. $4\frac{14}{15}$ $15\frac{5}{7}$ $6\frac{2}{3}$ $7\frac{3}{4}$
5. $10\frac{1}{2}$ $27\frac{8}{11}$ $7\frac{7}{10}$ $2\frac{2}{3}$
6. $2\frac{5}{12}$ $11\frac{1}{2}$ $4\frac{7}{10}$ $2\frac{11}{12}$
7. $5\frac{13}{20}$ $4\frac{5}{8}$ $4\frac{7}{9}$
8. $14\frac{5}{12}$ $18\frac{13}{14}$ $8\frac{7}{12}$
9. $5\frac{4}{5}$ $31\frac{38}{45}$ $8\frac{19}{42}$
10. $7\frac{23}{40}$ $13\frac{20}{33}$ $1\frac{7}{12}$

11. $\frac{23}{30}$ $3\frac{25}{36}$ $13\frac{43}{56}$
12. $6\frac{17}{24}$ $10\frac{17}{30}$ $6\frac{7}{8}$
13. $13\frac{5}{6}$ $\frac{17}{22}$ $1\frac{37}{56}$
14. $16\frac{13}{20}$ $5\frac{7}{18}$ $14\frac{25}{48}$

Pages 37–38

1. $20\frac{7}{8}$ inches
2. $154\frac{1}{4}$ pounds
3. $489\frac{2}{5}$ miles
4. $3\frac{1}{3}$ yards
5. $8\frac{1}{12}$ feet
6. $3\frac{2}{3}$ rpm's
7. $55\frac{3}{8}$ pounds
8. $\frac{1}{8}$ pound
9. $43\frac{1}{6}$ feet
10. $16\frac{5}{6}$ feet
11. $7\frac{3}{4}$ miles
12. $2\frac{1}{4}$ miles
13. $\$2\frac{3}{8}$ million
14. $\$\frac{5}{8}$ million
15. No. The total dimensions are $38\frac{1}{8}$ inches.
16. Yes. The total dimensions are $36\frac{1}{2}$ inches.

Page 39

1. $\frac{8}{15}$ $\frac{10}{63}$ $\frac{7}{80}$ $\frac{15}{88}$
2. $\frac{1}{15}$ $\frac{16}{63}$ $\frac{25}{48}$ $\frac{9}{40}$
3. $\frac{14}{45}$ $\frac{21}{64}$ $\frac{5}{36}$ $\frac{16}{81}$
4. $\frac{9}{40}$ $\frac{5}{42}$ $\frac{10}{81}$
5. $\frac{16}{75}$ $\frac{14}{135}$ $\frac{8}{63}$

Pages 40–41

1. $\frac{3}{10}$ $\frac{4}{21}$ $\frac{7}{16}$ $\frac{5}{14}$
2. $\frac{2}{15}$ $\frac{16}{39}$ $\frac{45}{77}$ $\frac{4}{65}$
3. $\frac{1}{6}$ $\frac{3}{8}$ $\frac{1}{4}$ $\frac{3}{4}$
4. $\frac{9}{20}$ $\frac{4}{15}$ $\frac{3}{8}$ $\frac{5}{18}$
5. $\frac{3}{10}$ $\frac{8}{11}$ $\frac{2}{5}$ $\frac{3}{20}$
6. $\frac{9}{52}$ $\frac{2}{7}$ $\frac{5}{7}$ $\frac{1}{3}$
7. $\frac{15}{32}$ $\frac{1}{9}$ $\frac{8}{15}$
8. $\frac{3}{8}$ $\frac{7}{60}$ $\frac{3}{32}$
9. $\frac{4}{45}$ $\frac{9}{100}$ $\frac{2}{9}$
10. $\frac{5}{84}$ $\frac{3}{25}$ $\frac{19}{120}$
11. $\frac{5}{27}$ $\frac{14}{99}$ $\frac{1}{16}$

Page 42

1. $1\frac{5}{7}$ $2\frac{1}{4}$ $6\frac{2}{3}$ $2\frac{2}{5}$
2. 10 10 $1\frac{1}{3}$ 24
3. 21 $5\frac{1}{2}$ 14 $11\frac{1}{4}$
4. $8\frac{1}{6}$ $3\frac{1}{3}$ 21 $1\frac{4}{5}$

Page 43

1. $\frac{3}{8}$ $\frac{10}{21}$ $1\frac{31}{32}$ $1\frac{13}{20}$
2. $1\frac{2}{3}$ $\frac{3}{4}$ $4\frac{3}{8}$ $5\frac{1}{7}$
3. $2\frac{4}{5}$ 25 $16\frac{1}{4}$ $38\frac{1}{2}$
4. 4 $22\frac{1}{2}$ 84

Page 44

Estimates and exact answers are given.

1. 18 and $16\frac{1}{2}$ 12 and $12\frac{1}{2}$ 45 and 48   16 and $14\frac{2}{3}$
2. 25 and 23   18 and $18\frac{2}{3}$ 24 and $22\frac{1}{2}$ 60 and $61\frac{1}{2}$
3. 4 and $4\frac{1}{6}$ 10 and 12   15 and $12\frac{3}{5}$ 4 and 5
4. 6 and 6   16 and $16\frac{2}{3}$ 12 and $9\frac{5}{8}$ 9 and $8\frac{5}{8}$

Page 45–46

1. 32 hours
2. 184 miles
3. 200 pounds
4. 171 inches
5. c. a little under $12
6. $11.50
7. b. a little over $45
8. 27 miles
9. $9\frac{1}{2}$ yards
10. $2\frac{3}{4}$ yards
11. $51.20
12. $9.60
13. $3\frac{1}{2}$ hours
14. $33.60
15. $84.80
16. $8,800
17. $3,800
18. $79,200

Page 48

1. $1\frac{1}{14}$ $\frac{2}{3}$ $\frac{11}{24}$ $\frac{7}{12}$
2. $1\frac{1}{10}$ 4 $\frac{28}{39}$ $1\frac{1}{5}$
3. $1\frac{23}{40}$ $1\frac{4}{45}$ $1\frac{2}{7}$ $1\frac{1}{5}$
4. $\frac{3}{28}$ 4 $3\frac{1}{30}$ $2\frac{2}{15}$
5. $\frac{35}{66}$ $1\frac{29}{49}$ $8\frac{1}{2}$ $\frac{3}{16}$
6. $\frac{7}{20}$ $\frac{3}{5}$ $1\frac{1}{3}$ $1\frac{1}{63}$

Page 50

1. 30 27 $6\frac{2}{3}$ 9
2. $21\frac{1}{3}$ 30 34 36
3. 50 84 $37\frac{1}{2}$ 66
4. 90 36 $26\frac{2}{3}$ $31\frac{1}{2}$
5. 168 $47\frac{1}{2}$ $16\frac{1}{2}$ $13\frac{1}{3}$
6. 32 $5\frac{1}{3}$ $8\frac{1}{3}$ $58\frac{1}{3}$

Page 52

1. $\frac{1}{5}$ $\frac{1}{9}$ $\frac{2}{19}$ $\frac{1}{8}$
2. $\frac{1}{36}$ $\frac{3}{28}$ $\frac{1}{12}$ $\frac{4}{13}$
3. $\frac{1}{22}$ $\frac{1}{25}$ $\frac{1}{8}$ $\frac{2}{39}$
4. $\frac{5}{126}$ $\frac{1}{40}$ $\frac{2}{75}$ $\frac{3}{125}$
5. $\frac{1}{15}$ $\frac{1}{39}$ $\frac{1}{51}$ $\frac{3}{88}$
6. $\frac{1}{77}$ $\frac{1}{48}$ $\frac{1}{54}$ $\frac{1}{120}$

Pages 53–54

1. 2 $2\frac{1}{2}$ $4\frac{2}{5}$ $19\frac{1}{2}$
2. $\frac{2}{5}$ $\frac{5}{6}$ $\frac{4}{21}$ $\frac{4}{27}$
3. $\frac{1}{2}$ $\frac{4}{5}$ $\frac{7}{30}$ $\frac{3}{20}$
4. $7\frac{1}{2}$ $8\frac{3}{4}$ $4\frac{4}{5}$ $14\frac{2}{3}$
5. $3\frac{1}{3}$ $3\frac{6}{7}$ $1\frac{7}{15}$ $\frac{4}{5}$
6. $1\frac{1}{8}$ 2 $1\frac{19}{30}$ $2\frac{4}{5}$
7. 3 $\frac{1}{2}$ $1\frac{19}{21}$ 4
8. $2\frac{2}{3}$ 3 $2\frac{1}{4}$ $1\frac{1}{39}$
9. $2\frac{1}{45}$ $1\frac{13}{42}$ $5\frac{7}{18}$ $1\frac{43}{61}$
10. $2\frac{11}{32}$ $1\frac{23}{41}$ $1\frac{29}{41}$ $2\frac{13}{36}$

Page 55

1. 15 88
2. 27 72
3. 20 64
4. 75 24
5. 96 66
6. 100 36
7. 150 60

Pages 56–57

1. 6 pieces
2. $1\frac{1}{2}$ pounds
3. 6 suits
4. 6 loaves
5. 32 cans
6. 9 strips
7. 4 dresses (with some material left)
8. 24 problems
9. $3,600
10. $2,700
11. 27 students
12. 9 students
13. 150 workers
14. 60 workers
15. $5\frac{1}{4}$ pounds
16. $1\frac{3}{4}$ pounds
17. $\frac{3}{4}$ million
18. $\frac{1}{2}$ million

Pages 58–59, Fractions Review

1. $\frac{7}{12}$
2. $\frac{7}{15}, \frac{4}{9}$
3. $\frac{9}{16}$
4. $4\frac{1}{6}$
5. $\frac{93}{8}$
6. $\frac{9}{12}$
7. $19\frac{7}{8}$
8. $20\frac{23}{30}$
9. greater than 1
10. $2\frac{5}{12}$ hours
11. $13\frac{5}{16}$ pounds
12. $5\frac{19}{40}$
13. $5\frac{6}{11}$
14. $8\frac{7}{18}$
15. $\frac{3}{4}$ pound
16. $1\frac{5}{6}$ miles
17. $\frac{20}{63}$
18. $\frac{2}{5}$
19. $3\frac{1}{3}$
20. 18
21. 65 pounds
22. 96¢
23. $\frac{32}{35}$
24. $31\frac{1}{2}$
25. $\frac{1}{26}$
26. $\frac{15}{28}$
27. 75
28. 6 bookcases
29. $12

Pages 60–61, Decimal Skills Inventory

1. 0.076
2. $3\frac{1}{25}$
3. $0.41\frac{2}{3}$
4. 0.08
5. 0.07, 0.08, 0.087, 0.7
6. 2.1
7. 4.439
8. 23.953
9. 12.1 pounds
10. 84.1°
11. 9.143
12. 11.63
13. 1.15 yards
14. 286.8 miles
15. 10.971
16. 0.0228
17. 49.2
18. 144 miles
19. $62.35
20. 0.86
21. 7.3
22. 370
23. 200
24. 0.496
25. $2.60
26. 5 yards

Page 63

1. 3 5 1 6
2. 4 2 3 1
3. 6 7 3 5
4. 9 7 2 3
5. 4 9 1 3
6. 3 8 5 6

7. 9 tenths
8. 7 thousandths

Page 64

1. tenths tenths hundredths
2. hundredths hundredths thousandths
3. thousandths ten-thousandths
4. thousandths ten-thousandths
5. hundredths thousandths
6. tenths ten-thousandths
7. five tenths   two and nine tenths
8. seven hundredths   three and twelve hundredths
9. sixteen thousandths   one and three thousandths
10. nine thousandths   seven and twenty-one thousandths
11. sixteen ten-thousandths   ten and four hundred two thousandths

Page 65

1. 0.7   4.9
2. 0.63   0.022
3. 0.02   0.85
4. 0.4   0.019
5. 12.3   0.41
6. 1.05   0.206
7. 48.9   0.008
8. 0.304   11.07
9. 0.0015   4.013
10. 230.1   0.0071
11. 0.047   8.0002
12. 0.00005   0.000019

Page 66

1. c. 5.006
2. a. 3.105
3. d. 700.4
4. b. 40.092
5. d. both a and b
6. b. 0.034

Page 67

1. $\frac{2}{25}$ $\frac{3}{8}$ $\frac{3}{625}$

2. $3\frac{3}{5}$ $9\frac{43}{50}$ $10\frac{1}{500}$

3. $\frac{17}{200}$ $5\frac{2}{25}$ $\frac{1}{400}$

4. $7\frac{1}{5}$ $\frac{3}{20}$ $8\frac{4}{25}$

5. $\frac{81}{25,000}$ $19\frac{393}{5,000}$ $123\frac{231}{500}$

6. $16\frac{1}{25,000}$ $7\frac{11}{50}$ $3\frac{1}{125,000}$

7. $2,036\frac{4}{5}$ $48\frac{1}{50}$ $3\frac{3}{40}$

Page 68

1. 0.25   0.4   0.625 or $0.62\frac{1}{2}$ $0.33\frac{1}{3}$

2. $0.22\frac{2}{9}$ 0.24 $0.16\frac{2}{3}$ 0.375 or $0.37\frac{1}{2}$

3. $0.83\frac{1}{3}$ 0.3 $0.57\frac{1}{7}$ $0.41\frac{2}{3}$

4. 0.6   0.9 $0.08\frac{1}{3}$ $0.44\frac{4}{9}$

5. $0.13\frac{1}{3}$ 0.75   0.125 or $0.12\frac{1}{2}$ 0.48

Page 69

1. 0.8   0.1666666   0.4166666   0.9

2. 0.375   0.2222222   0.3125   0.3333333

3. 0.28   0.2   0.875   0.3

4. 2.5   1.6   1.3333333   1.75

5. 1.8333333   1.3   1.125   6.5

Page 70

1. 0.04   0.99   0.707

2. 0.33   0.11   0.2

3. 0.006   0.4   0.07

4. 0.03, 0.033, 0.303, 0.33   0.08, 0.082, 0.28, 0.8

5. 0.061, 0.106, 0.16, 0.6   0.007, 0.017, 0.02, 0.2

6. 0.045, 0.4, 0.405, 0.45   0.04, 0.304, 0.32, 0.4

7. 0.0072, 0.02, 0.027, 0.07   0.026, 0.06, 0.0602, 0.2

Page 72

1. 4.3   0.6   516.2   27.1

2. 0.58   12.49   0.09   2.10

3. 23.486   0.054   5.407   0.003

4. 17   2   357   200

5. $14 $10 $2 $347

6. $2.80 $63.50 $1.00 $5.30

7. $0.99 $4.68 $23.95 $1.09

8. 49.1   49.08   49.076   49.0758   49

9. 0.63   0.67   0.43   0.78

10. 0.083   0.833   0.188   0.133

Page 73

1. 1.207   25.18

2. 134.64   39.617

3. 24.313   65.303

4. 75.449   18.8097

5. 132.543   93.277

6. 23.458   0.5069

7. 37.815   22.135

Page 74

1. 10.66 inches

2. 1,200 miles

3. 76.9 inches

4. 9.7 pounds

5. 121.5 miles

6. 103.1°

7. 7.02 kilograms

8. 130.2 million people

Page 75

1. 0.44   0.6367   0.52

2. 0.122   54.36   88.534

3. 11.064   0.953   12.068

4. 7.769   0.068   2.507

5. 88.515   3.0014   0.0708

6. 0.236   0.017   1.193

7. 0.0644   0.422   0.541

Page 76

Estimates and exact answers are given.

1. 5.0 and 5.015   17.6 and 17.637

2. 0.8 and 0.797   0.2 and 0.248

3. 19.3 and 19.2885   6.8 and 6.776

4. 155 and 155.308   32 and 31.625

5. 19 and 19.237   3 and 3.604

6. 1.9 and 1.902   0.56 and 0.5534

Pages 77–78

1. 6.4 years
2. 79.5 sq mi
3. 0.33 meter
4. 12.8 miles
5. 402.7 miles
6. 123.15 meters
7. 5.8 million
8. $0.37
9. 1.89 kilograms
10. 0.11 kilogram under
11. $0.24
12. $0.48
13. 21.5 million
14. 6.4 inches
15. 5.62 inches
16. 1.05 million

Pages 79–81

1. 15.2   8.28   40.2   42.4   5.88
2. 1.23   39   5.31   34.4   1.14
3. 277.6   20.23   3.306   542.7   28.72
4. 63.42   1.008   626.4   39.12   1.401
5. 142.5   27.72   1,341   560.7   550.2
6. 0.054   0.035   0.0012   0.0032   0.0016
7. 1.12   0.0584   6.44   0.0348   0.198
8. 29.26   0.312   0.258   4.428   1.388
9. 11.7   2.496   8.188   2.414   0.2184
10. 0.486   2.184   26.46   0.1411   6.072
11. 12.04   4.592   4.104
12. 0.5589   1.692   8.235
13. 48.84   296.64   0.46774
14. 66.138   253.176   273.604
15. 57.932   3.66912   7,252.3
16. 36.2142   72.89   3.44787
17. 2.7712   0.14904   44.7468
18. 836.368   0.047413   112.274
19. 8.29376   17,210.57   2.8764

Page 82

1. 8   0.9   36.4   7.21
2. 3   27.5   890   86.3
3. 900   2,360   475   1,600
4. 3.4   124   3,850   60
5. $12.50 $60 $2,250 $30

Page 83

Estimates and exact answers are given.

1. 1.5 and 1.41   0.072 and 0.0747   4.8 and 5.12
2. 0.48 and 0.474   0.18 and 0.174   1.4 and 1.274
3. 20 and 19.24   2.4 and 2.542   0.35 and 0.3922
4. 0.28 and 0.2812   6.3 and 6.097   0.32 and 0.3564
5. 10 and 9.9164   16 and 17.507   6.3 and 6.2652

Pages 84–85

1. 30.5 cm
2. $73.50
3. 40 km
4. 1,061.5 miles
5. 72 kg
6. 1,000 pounds
7. $34.27
8. $56.95
9. 69 meters
10. $3.78
11. $5.02
12. $4.98
13. $135.10
14. $151.03
15. 34,500
16. 3.3 gallons
17. 9.9 gallons
18. $11.93
19. $22.68

Page 86

1. 2.3   7.8   0.096   8.25
2. 0.024   49.6   3.89   0.631
3. 4.8   0.36   0.08   5.7
4. 0.183   36.4   6.03   0.517

Pages 87–88

1. 9.6   38   0.7   6.9
2. 0.28   14   0.83   0.09
3. 14.7   1.93   605   12.8
4. 1.3   0.24   37   2.9
5. 760   480   2,700   9,640
6. 13,300   4   720   85
7. 325   71,400   935   2,080
8. 490   3,070   560   9,310
9. 0.06   2.07   40.4   0.182

Page 89

1. 70   400   3,700   6,400
2. 9,000   8,000   3,900   6,280
3. 200   4,000   2,000   28
4. 460   7,200   500   420
5. 62,000   78,000   5,900   83,000

Page 90

1. 0.09   3.6   2.73   0.004
2. 0.142   0.013   7.28   0.006
3. 0.0375   0.0018   0.002   0.428
4. 1.345   0.0032   6.954   0.0158
5. $0.29 $6.50 $0.54 $0.02

Page 91

1. 1.1   11.4   3.3
2. 0.1   0.3   7.1
3. 3.1   0.2   138.5
4. 1.4   29.4   22.2
5. 1.8   1.4   78.8

Pages 92–93

1. 127.2 pounds
2. 249.5 miles
3. $9.60
4. 38.5 hours
5. 384 mph
6. $1.60
7. 23 miles
8. 18 inches
9. .327
10. .311
11. 29.6 points per game
12. 21.4 points per game
13. 21.6 miles per gallon
14. 39 chairs per worker
15. 167 pieces per hour

Pages 94–95, Cumulative Review

1. $8\frac{19}{24}$
2. $3\frac{17}{18}$
3. 12
4. 4
5. 0.0014
6. $\frac{2}{125}$
7. 0.4375
8. 0.02
9. 0.013, 0.03, 0.031, 0.1
10. 12.4
11. 21.356
12. 10.6973
13. 11.35 pounds
14. 12.203
15. 2.346
16. 1.984 inches
17. 2.844
18. 2,080
19. 720
20. 16.5 centimeters
21. $6.75
22. 4.09
23. 7.2
24. 6
25. 250
26. 0.00513
27. 34.5 mph
28. $15.70

Pages 96–97, Percent Skills Inventory

1. 1.7%
2. 0.04
3. $62\frac{1}{2}$%
4. $\frac{3}{25}$
5. $\frac{1}{12}$
6. 12
7. 11.5
8. 36
9. $0.84
10. $563
11. $33\frac{1}{3}$%
12. 8%
13. 11%
14. $66\frac{2}{3}$%
15. 80
16. 56
17. $3,040
18. $26.50

Page 98

1. 100
2. 49%
3. 100
4. 100%
5. 100%
6. 50%

Page 99

1. 32%   9%   60%   13.6%
2. 0.5% $37\frac{1}{2}$% $8\frac{1}{3}$%   4.5%
3. 0.16%   0.03%   2.5% $33\frac{1}{3}$%
4. 12.5%   3.75%   0.9%   20%
5. 0.1 = 10%   0.2 = 20%   0.01 = 1%
   0.3 = 30%   0.4 = 40%   0.25 = 25%
   0.7 = 70%   0.6 = 60%   0.5 = 50%
   0.9 = 90%   0.8 = 80%   0.75 = 75%

Page 100

1. 0.2   0.35   0.08   0.6
2. 0.035   0.004   0.0003   0.216
3. $0.62\frac{1}{2}$ $0.06\frac{2}{3}$ 0.028   0.19
4. 0.07   0.015   2.0   0.142
5. 50% = 0.5   5% = 0.05   37.5% = 0.375
   25% = 0.25   1% = 0.01   62.5% = 0.625
   75% = 0.75   100% = 1.0   87.5% = 0.875
   20% = 0.2   80% = 0.8   12.5% = 0.125

Page 101

1. 40%   25% $33\frac{1}{3}$% $37\frac{1}{2}$%
2. 24% $66\frac{2}{3}$% $83\frac{1}{3}$% $12\frac{1}{2}$%
3. 90% $87\frac{1}{2}$%   55% $41\frac{2}{3}$%
4. $16\frac{2}{3}$%   80%   70% $8\frac{1}{3}$%
5. $62\frac{1}{2}$% $44\frac{4}{9}$% $42\frac{6}{7}$%   45%
6. 16%   30%   60%   18%

Page 102

1. $\frac{7}{20}$ $\frac{1}{5}$ $\frac{1}{8}$ $\frac{3}{50}$

2. $\frac{1}{6}$ $\frac{1}{100}$ $\frac{9}{10}$ $\frac{3}{8}$

3. $\frac{3}{25}$ $\frac{99}{100}$ $\frac{2}{3}$ $\frac{9}{200}$

4. $\frac{4}{5}$ $\frac{1}{3}$ $\frac{1}{25}$ $\frac{1}{12}$

Page 103

$\frac{1}{2} = 50\%$ $\qquad$ $\frac{1}{8} = 12\frac{1}{2}\%$

$\frac{1}{4} = 25\%$ $\qquad$ $\frac{3}{8} = 37\frac{1}{2}\%$

$\frac{3}{4} = 75\%$ $\qquad$ $\frac{5}{8} = 62\frac{1}{2}\%$

$\qquad$ $\frac{7}{8} = 87\frac{1}{2}\%$

$\frac{1}{5} = 20\%$ $\qquad$ $\frac{1}{10} = 10\%$

$\frac{2}{5} = 40\%$ $\qquad$ $\frac{3}{10} = 30\%$

$\frac{3}{5} = 60\%$ $\qquad$ $\frac{7}{10} = 70\%$

$\frac{4}{5} = 80\%$ $\qquad$ $\frac{9}{10} = 90\%$

$\frac{1}{3} = 33\frac{1}{3}\%$ $\qquad$ $\frac{1}{6} = 16\frac{2}{3}\%$

$\frac{2}{3} = 66\frac{2}{3}\%$ $\qquad$ $\frac{5}{6} = 83\frac{1}{3}\%$

Pages 104–105

1. 6   67.55   78

2. 7.2   7.5   24

3. 510   400   209

4. 168   403   799

5. 10.14   0.448   13.554

6. 25   12   14

7. 270   525   3

8. 21   60   175

9. 3 $3\frac{3}{4}$ 110

Page 106

1. 24   230   7

2. 90   130   40

3. 90   400   30

4. 17   70   300

5. 120   241   900

Page 107

1. 24 days

2. $4,750

3. 6 questions

4. 351 members

5. 6 classes

6. $168

7. $300

8. 10 days

9. $9\frac{3}{4}$ pounds

Page 108

1. $140\frac{1}{4}$ pounds

2. $38.40

3. $2.65

4. $295.20

5. $622.08

6. $131,760

7. $49.30

8. 1.32 million

9. $1,020

Page 109

1. $22.75

2. 205 people

3. $13.24

4. $67.91

5. 48 employees

6. 132 people

Pages 110–111

1. 50%   25% $33\frac{1}{3}\%$

2. 10% $16\frac{2}{3}\%$ $12\frac{1}{2}\%$

3. 80%   40% $66\frac{2}{3}\%$

4. $83\frac{1}{3}\%$ 75% $87\frac{1}{2}\%$

5. $87\frac{1}{2}\%$ 90%   80%

6. 7%   6%   9%

7. 35%   38%   32%

8. $58\frac{1}{3}\%$ 100% $44\frac{4}{9}\%$

9. $83\frac{1}{3}\%$ $42\frac{6}{7}\%$ 90%

10. 2%   6% $8\frac{1}{3}\%$

11. 20%   80% $22\frac{1}{2}\%$

12. $16\frac{2}{3}\%$ 26%   0.396%

Pages 112–113

1. 75%

2. 4%

3. $62\frac{1}{2}\%$

4. 90%

5. 8%

6. 5%

7. $33\frac{1}{3}\%$

8. $66\frac{2}{3}\%$

9. 25%

10. 55%

11. 45%

12. $62\frac{1}{2}\%$

13. $8\frac{1}{3}\%$

14. 25%

15. 75%

16. $12\frac{1}{2}\%$

17. 5%

18. $16\frac{2}{3}\%$

19. $8\frac{1}{3}\%$

20. $33\frac{1}{3}\%$

Page 114

1. 25%
2. 21%
3. 30%
4. $12\frac{1}{2}$%
5. $33\frac{1}{3}$%
6. 400%

Pages 115–116

1. 32   90
2. 64   125
3. 150   80
4. 63   24
5. 75   1,280
6. 1,800   1,400
7. 64   180
8. 480   240
9. 192   1,500
10. 305   1,050
11. 438   875

Pages 117–118

1. $160
2. 30 problems
3. $2,500
4. 390 seats
5. $60
6. 120 members
7. $2,900
8. $120,000
9. 2,250 radios
10. 18,000 people
11. 3,000 miles
12. $2,000
13. $35
14. $455
15. $100.10

Pages 119–120

1. %, 50%   P, 33
2. P, 90   %, 20%
3. W, 60   P, 340
4. P, 15   %, 80%
5. %, $33\frac{1}{3}$%   W, 460
6. P, 30 employees
7. %, 75%
8. P, $1.45
9. W, $1,600
10. %, 15%
11. P, 198 people
12. W, 1,200 seats

Pages 121–122, Cumulative Review

1. $13\frac{7}{8}$
2. $4\frac{2}{5}$
3. $1\frac{3}{4}$
4. 1.30
5. 0.325
6. 1.5
7. 12.3%
8. 0.056
9. $58\frac{1}{3}$%
10. $\frac{21}{25}$
11. $\frac{5}{16}$
12. 24.3
13. 51.98
14. c. $72 \div 8$
15. $24.75
16. 15,000 voters
17. $62\frac{1}{2}$%
18. $8\frac{1}{2}$%
19. 75%
20. $62\frac{1}{2}$%
21. 200
22. 384
23. 420 miles
24. 320 jackets

Pages 123–126, Posttest A

1. $\frac{4}{9}$
2. $20\frac{1}{24}$
3. less than 1
4. $59\frac{1}{6}$ inches
5. $41\frac{35}{36}$
6. $6\frac{15}{16}$
7. $\frac{1}{15}$
8. $40\frac{1}{2}$
9. 24
10. $50.75
11. $\frac{1}{25}$
12. $4\frac{1}{5}$
13. 48 bags
14. $540
15. 50.208
16. 0.02, 0.021, 0.12, 0.2
17. 309.799
18. 128.1 pounds
19. 39.613
20. 17.8
21. 136.2 miles
22. 3.8912
23. 5.6
24. $3.60
25. 0.26
26. 19.3
27. 14.1
28. 15 miles
29. 0.079
30. $56\frac{1}{4}$%
31. $\frac{1}{6}$
32. 54.72
33. 12
34. b. $84 \div 4$
35. $110.72
36. $83\frac{1}{3}$%
37. $62\frac{1}{2}$%
38. 160
39. $250,000

Pages 128–132, Posttest B

1. c. $\frac{2}{3}$
2. a. $16\frac{17}{48}$
3. a. greater than 1
4. d. $52\frac{1}{16}$ pounds
5. c. $4\frac{8}{15}$
6. b. $5\frac{1}{2}$ inches
7. d. $\frac{3}{8}$
8. b. $2\frac{3}{4}$
9. d. 14
10. a. $5\frac{1}{4}$ pounds
11. c. $\frac{4}{5}$
12. d. $2\frac{2}{5}$
13. d. 200 bags
14. a. 320
15. c. 7.051
16. b. 0.004, 0.06, 0.064, 0.4
17. c. 26.392
18. b. 7.593 billion
19. d. 12.214
20. a. 2.57
21. b. 0.086 meter
22. a. 54.384
23. c. 24.4
24. d. $8.47
25. c. 4.3
26. b. 4
27. c. 6.54
28. d. 58 mph
29. c. 0.026
30. a. $42\frac{6}{7}\%$
31. d. $\frac{5}{16}$
32. c. 294
33. d. 210
34. c. $180 \div 6$
35. a. $87\frac{1}{2}\%$
36. d. 75%
37. c. 120
38. b. 280

Page 134

1. C—$1\frac{5}{8}$ inches
   D—2 inches
   E—$2\frac{1}{4}$ inches
   F—$2\frac{7}{8}$ inches
   G—$3\frac{1}{8}$ inches
   H—$3\frac{7}{16}$ inches
   I—$3\frac{15}{16}$ inches
   J—$4\frac{1}{2}$ inches
   K—$4\frac{13}{16}$ inches
   L—$5\frac{9}{16}$ inches
2. $\frac{3}{8}$ inch
3. $\frac{9}{16}$ inch
4. $1\frac{1}{16}$ inches

Page 135

1. C—2.9 centimeters
   D—3.4 centimeters
   E—4.0 centimeters
   F—5.5 centimeters
   G—7.1 centimeters
   H—7.5 centimeters
   I—10.4 centimeters
   J—11.7 centimeters
   K—13.2 centimeters
   L—15.0 centimeters
2. 1.1 centimeters
3. 1.6 centimeters
4. 1.5 centimeters

Pages 136–137

1. $21\frac{1}{3}$ inches
2. $18\frac{1}{4}$ feet
3. 39 inches
4. 24 meters
5. $228
6. $185\frac{1}{2}$ yards
7. 29.8 centimeters
8. 25 yards
9. 10 inches
10. 7 meters

Pages 138–139

1. 20 sq ft
2. 17.36 sq cm
3. 30 sq in.
4. 28 sq ft
5. 39.6 sq m
6. $649.44
7. $7\frac{1}{2}$ sq yd
8. 12.96 sq m
9. $5\frac{4}{9}$ sq ft
10. $12\frac{1}{4}$ sq in.

Pages 140–141

1. 10 cu ft
2. 531.25 cu ft
3. 918 cu ft
4. 594 cu in.
5. 1,500 cu in.
6. $7\frac{1}{2}$ cu in.
7. 200 boxes
8. 1,279.08 cu m
9. 84 cu ft
10. 26 cu ft

Pages 142–143

1. 176 yards
2. 110 feet
3. $236.50
4. $31\frac{3}{7}$ inches
5. 11 feet
6. $12.98
7. 88 inches
8. 44 inches
9. $94\frac{2}{7}$ feet

Pages 144–145

1. 154 sq ft
2. $314\frac{2}{7}$ sq ft
3. 616 tiles
4. $78\frac{4}{7}$ sq ft
5. $147.84
6. 13.86 sq m
7. $38\frac{1}{2}$ sq yd
8. $1,732.50
9. $3\frac{1}{7}$ sq ft
10. $\frac{11}{14}$ sq ft

Page 146

1. 2 cups flour $2\frac{2}{3}$ cups egg whites

   3 cups sugar $3\frac{1}{3}$ teaspoons cream of tartar

   $\frac{1}{2}$ teaspoon salt $2\frac{1}{2}$ teaspoons vanilla

2. $\frac{1}{2}$ cup flour $\frac{2}{3}$ cup egg whites

   $\frac{3}{4}$ cup sugar $\frac{5}{6}$ teaspoon cream of tartar

   $\frac{1}{8}$ teaspoon salt $\frac{5}{8}$ teaspoon vanilla

3. 5 cups flour $6\frac{2}{3}$ cups egg whites

   $7\frac{1}{2}$ cups sugar $8\frac{1}{3}$ teaspoons cream of tartar

   $1\frac{1}{4}$ teaspoons salt $6\frac{1}{4}$ teaspoons vanilla

Pages 147–149

1. 870 km	11. 10 gal
2. 68 sq m	12. 1.33 lb
3. 19 l	13. 3,434 mi
4. 27.9 cm; 21.6 cm	14. 238,000 mi
5. 81 kg	15. 80.7 sq ft
6. 339 sq km	16. 72.8 in.
7. 34 g	17. 1.6 qt
8. 0.7 l	18. 3,490 sq mi
9. 38 cm	19. 2.4 oz
10. 7.7 lb	20. 1,076 sq ft

Page 151

1. $80	5. $13.50
2. $67.50	6. $172.50
3. $5	7. $79.80
4. $67	8. $57

Page 152

1. $18
2. $12.50
3. $105
4. $3.60
5. $18.40

Page 153

1. $162
2. $275
3. $17.50
4. $525
5. $18

Page 155

1. a. $12	b. $812
2. a. $12.18	b. $824.18
3. a. $12.36	b. $836.54
4. a. $12.55	b. $849.09
5. a. $24	b. $1,224
6. a. $24.48	b. $1,248.48
7. a. $24.97	b. $1,273.45
8. a. $25.47	b. $1,298.92
9. a. $1,000	b. $21,000
10. a. $1,050	b. $22,050
11. a. $1,102.50	b. $23,152.50
12. a. $1,157.63	b. $24,310.13

Page 157

1. a. 0.89\frac{1}{2}$
   b. $0.83
   c. 0.79\frac{1}{2}$
   d. Sam's Store

2. a. 0.28\frac{4}{7}$
   b. 0.29\frac{2}{3}$
   c. 0.24\frac{1}{2}$
   d. Sam's Store

3. a. 1.04\frac{1}{2}$
   b. 0.99\frac{1}{2}$
   c. $1.05
   d. Gert's Groceries

Page 159

1. 38%	7. 50%
2. 50%	8. $22\frac{2}{9}$%
3. $42\frac{6}{7}$%	9. 20%
4. $27\frac{3}{11}$%	10. 24%
5. $29\frac{17}{27}$%	11. $17\frac{1}{7}$%
6. $46\frac{2}{3}$%	

Pages 160–161

1. $19.50	**4.** $33.30
2. $58.50	**5.** $150.30
3. $16.65	**6.** $162.32

7.

For credit to the Account of			Dollars	Cents
	Cash Include Coupons		30	00
DEBORAH ROBINSON PH. 123-555-7890 9876 S. Wentworth Avenue Clarksville, OH 11223	Checks List Each Check 1		535	70
Bank Use Only	2			
Chk	3			
Less Dep	4			
Ret'd	5			
	6			
Date: February 4, 2000	Units 7			
CHEMICAL BANK Checking Account Deposit	Total		565	70
	Less Cash Received		—	
	Net Deposit		565	70

8.

DEBORAH ROBINSON
PH. 123-555-7890
9876 S. Wentworth Avenue
Clarksville, OH 11223

No. 004
Feb. 6 20 00 1-12/210

PAY TO THE ORDER OF   The Friendly Furniture Store $ 162.32
One hundred sixty-two and 32/100 ————— DOLLARS

CHEMICAL BANK

FOR two lamps and high chair   Deborah Robinson

CHECK NO.	DATE	CHECK ISSUED TO	AMOUNT OF CHECK		√ T	FEE (IF ANY)		AMOUNT OF DEPOSIT		BALANCE	
										585	00
001	1/21	Telephone Company	35	70						549	30
002	1/29	Utility Company	15	36						533	94
003	2/1	Rental Agent	345	00						188	94
	2/4	Deposit						565	70	754	64
004	2/6	Friendly Furniture Store	162	32						592	32

page 163

1. $8,080	**6.** $34,321
2. $4,524	**7.** $17,806.26
3. $19,249	**8.** $23,747.72
4. $3,225	**9.** $15,276
5. $10,239.64	**10.** $2,333.25

Pages 164–165

1. $3,358.30	**4.** $331.10
2. $1,371.70	**5.** $17,319.25
3. $969.65	

6.

OMB No 1545-0008		
a Control number	1 Wages, tips, other compensation $23,650	2 Federal income tax withheld $3,358.30
	3 Social security wages $23,650	4 Social security tax withheld $1,371.70
	5 Medicare wages and tips $23,650	6 Medicare tax withheld $300

c Employer's name, address, and ZIP code

Colver Products
333 East 49th Street
New York, N.Y. 10017

7 Social security tips None	8 Allocated tips None	9 Advance EIC payment None
10 Dependent care benefits None	11 Nonqualified plans None	12 Benefits included in Box 1 None
b Employer's identification number 13-5009-340	d Employee's social security number 123-45-6789	
13 See Instrs. for Box 13	14 Other None	

e Employee's name, address, and ZIP code

Peter Cheung
5 East Third Street
New York, N.Y. 10003

15 Statutory employee	Deceased	Pension plan X	Legal rep	942 emp	Subtotal	Deferred compensation
1999	16 State N.Y.	Employer's state I.D. No. 21-4952		17 State wages, tips, etc. $23,650		
W-2 Wage and Tax Statement copy For EMPLOYEE'S State, City, or Local Income Tax Return		18 State income tax $969.65		19 Locality name New York		
		20 Local wages, tips, etc. $23,650		21 Local income tax $331.10		

Department of the Treasury—Internal Revenue Service

7. $189.20

PETER CHEUNG
5 East Third Street
New York, NY 10003

No. 021
April 15 19 99 1-12/210

PAY TO THE ORDER OF   Internal Revenue Service $ 189.20
One hundred eighty-nine and 20/100 ————— DOLLARS

CHEMICAL BANK

FOR taxes   Peter Cheung

Page 166

1. $14,000	Entertainment $2,160
2. $36,000	Clothes $3,600
Rent $7,200	Medical $4,320
Food $11,160	Savings $3,600
Utilities $1,800	Odds and Ends $2,160

Pages 167–168

1. a. $171.72	**4. a.** $481.95
b. $195.90	**b.** $582.72
c. $24.18	**c.** $100.77
2. a. $95.23	**5. a.** $307.35
b. $132	**b.** $360.39
c. $36.77	**c.** $53.04
3. a. $418.70	**6. a.** $240.45
b. $479.25	**b.** $336.64
c. $60.55	**c.** $96.19

Using a Calculator

A calculator is a useful tool for getting quick, exact answers. Remember that a fraction can be understood as a division problem.

EXAMPLE 1 Use a calculator to change $\frac{1}{8}$ to a decimal.

Press the following keys on a calculator: [1] [÷] [8] [=]

The calculator display should read $\boxed{0.125}$

EXAMPLE 2 Use a calculator to change $\frac{5}{6}$ to a decimal.

Press the following keys on a calculator: [5] [÷] [6] [=]

The calculator display should read $\boxed{0.8333333}$

EXAMPLE 3 Use a calculator to find $0.818 - 0.29$.

Press the following keys on a calculator: [·] [8] [1] [8] [−] [·] [2] [9] [=]

The calculator display should read $\boxed{0.528}$

EXAMPLE 4 Use a calculator to find 4.91×0.33.

Press the following keys on a calculator: [4] [·] [9] [1] [×] [·] [3] [3] [=]

The calculator display should read $\boxed{1.6203}$

EXAMPLE 5 Use a calculator to find $7.8 \div 0.9$.

Press the following keys on a calculator: [7] [·] [8] [÷] [·] [9] [=]

The calculator display should read $\boxed{8.6666666}$

EXAMPLE 6 Use a calculator to find 4.5% of 900.

Press the following keys on a calculator: [9] [0] [0] [×] [4] [·] [5] [%]

The calculator display should read $\boxed{40.5}$

Note: On some calculators you may have to press the [=] key after the [%] key.

Using Mental Math

Mental math refers to the problems you can do without pencil and paper and without a calculator. Below are examples of mental math problems that are covered in this book.

Multiplying Decimals by 10, 100, and 1,000

To multiply a decimal by 10, move the decimal point *one place to the right.*

EXAMPLE 1 $0.17 \times 10 = 1.7 = 1.7$

To multiply a decimal by 100, move the decimal point *two places to the right.* You may have to add zeros to get enough places.

EXAMPLE 2 $4.9 \times 100 = 4.90 = 490$

To multiply a decimal by 1,000, move the decimal point *three places to the right.*

EXAMPLE 3 $2.6 \times 1,000 = 2.600 = 2,600$

Dividing Decimals by 10, 100, and 1,000

To divide a decimal by 10, move the decimal point *one place to the left.*

EXAMPLE 4 $8.3 \div 10 = 8.3 = 0.83$

To divide a decimal by 100, move the decimal point *two places to the left.* You may have to add zeros to get enough places.

EXAMPLE 5 $4.57 \div 100 = 04.57 = 0.0457$

To divide a decimal by 1,000, move the decimal point *three places to the left.*

EXAMPLE 6 $16.9 \div 1,000 = 016.9 = 0.0169$

Shortcuts to Finding a Percent of a Number

To find a percent of a number with any percent on the following list, divide by the denominator of the fraction that the percent equals.

50%	$33\frac{1}{3}\%$	25%	20%	$16\frac{2}{3}\%$	$12\frac{1}{2}\%$	10%
$\frac{1}{2}$	$\frac{1}{3}$	$\frac{1}{4}$	$\frac{1}{5}$	$\frac{1}{6}$	$\frac{1}{8}$	$\frac{1}{10}$

EXAMPLE 7   What is $12\frac{1}{2}\%$ of 72?

$$12\frac{1}{2}\% \text{ of } 72 = 72 \div 8 = 9$$

Using Estimation

Estimating means finding an approximate answer. Estimating is a way to check whether an answer is reasonable. Most methods of estimating fraction and decimal problems involve rounding to the nearest whole number or rounding to a certain decimal place.

Estimating the Size of a Fraction

In a proper fraction, the numerator (top number) is less than the denominator (bottom number). The size of the numerator *compared* to the size of the denominator tells you something about the size of the fraction.

1. A fraction is *equal to one-half* when the numerator is exactly half the denominator.

EXAMPLES The fractions $\frac{3}{6}$, $\frac{4}{8}$, and $\frac{25}{50}$ are each equal to one-half.

2. A fraction is *less than one-half* when the numerator is less than half of the denominator.

EXAMPLES The fractions $\frac{1}{4}$, $\frac{3}{7}$, and $\frac{11}{40}$ are each less than one-half.

3. A fraction is *greater than one-half* when the numerator is more than half of the denominator.

EXAMPLES The fractions $\frac{4}{5}$, $\frac{7}{12}$, and $\frac{14}{25}$ are each greater than one-half.

Estimating Fraction Addition Problems

When you add two fractions, decide if the sum is equal to one whole (= 1), less than one whole (<1) or more than one whole (>1). Study these examples carefully.

When you add	Examples
$\frac{1}{2} + \frac{1}{2}$, the sum is 1.	$\frac{1}{2} + \frac{4}{8} = 1$
$\frac{1}{2}$ + a fraction that is *less* than $\frac{1}{2}$, the sum is *less than* 1.	$\frac{1}{2} + \frac{1}{4} < 1$
$\frac{1}{2}$ + a fraction that is *more* than $\frac{1}{2}$, the sum is *more than* 1.	$\frac{1}{2} + \frac{3}{4} > 1$

Estimating Fraction Multiplication Problems

To estimate a multiplication problem with mixed numbers, round each mixed number to the nearest whole number. Then use the whole numbers to multiply.

1. For a mixed number with a fraction of $\frac{1}{2}$ or more, round to the next whole number.

EXAMPLES $8\frac{2}{3} \rightarrow 9$ $\qquad$ $1\frac{7}{12} \rightarrow 2$ $\qquad$ $6\frac{1}{2} \rightarrow 7$

2. For a mixed number with a fraction less than $\frac{1}{2}$, drop the fraction and use the whole number.

EXAMPLES $4\frac{1}{6} \rightarrow 4$ $12\frac{1}{4} \rightarrow 12$ $1\frac{4}{9} \rightarrow 1$

EXAMPLE   Estimate an answer to $2\frac{7}{8} \times 6$.

STEP 1   Round $2\frac{7}{8}$ to the nearest whole number. $2\frac{7}{8} \rightarrow 3$

STEP 2   Multiply the rounded numbers. $3 \times 6 = 18$

STEP 3   Find the exact answer. Notice how close the estimate, 18, is to the exact answer, $17\frac{1}{4}$. $\dfrac{23}{\overset{}{\underset{4}{8}}} \times \dfrac{\overset{3}{\cancel{6}}}{1} = \dfrac{69}{4} = 17\dfrac{1}{4}$

Rounding Decimals

To round a decimal, do the following steps.

STEP 1   Underline the digit in the place you are rounding to.

STEP 2   **a.** If the digit to the right of the underlined digit is *greater than or equal to 5,* add 1 to the underlined digit.

   b. If the digit to the right of the underlined digit is *less than 5,* leave the underlined digit as is.

STEP 3   Drop all the digits to the right of the underlined digit.

EXAMPLE 1   Round 4.27 to the nearest tenth.

STEP 1   Underline 2, the digit in the tenths place. $4.\underline{2}7 \rightarrow \mathbf{4.3}$

STEP 2   The digit to the right of 2 is 7. Since 7 is greater than 5, add 1 to 2. $2 + 1 = 3$

STEP 3   Drop the digit to the right of 2.

EXAMPLE 2   Round 0.2849 to the nearest hundredth.

STEP 1   Underline 8, the digit in the hundredths place. $0.2\underline{8}49 \rightarrow \mathbf{0.28}$

STEP 2   The digit to the right of 8 is 4. Since 4 is less than 5, leave 8 as is.

STEP 3   Drop the digits to the right of 8.

Measurements and Formulas

In this book you find *standard* or *customary* units of measurement such as feet and pounds. You also find *metric* units such as meters and kilograms. The list below shows common units of measurements, their equivalents in other units, and their commonly used abbreviations.

Measures of Length

1 foot (ft or ')	= 12 inches (in. or ")
1 yard (yd)	= 36 inches
1 yard	= 3 feet
1 mile (mi)	= 5,280 feet
1 mile	= 1,760 yards
1 meter (m)	= 1,000 millimeters (mm)
1 meter	= 100 centimeters (cm)
1 kilometer (km)	= 1,000 meters

Measures of Weight

1 pound (lb)	= 16 ounces (oz)
1 ton (T)	= 2,000 pounds
1 kilogram (kg)	= 1,000 grams (g)

Liquid Measures

1 pint (pt)	= 16 ounces
1 pint	= 2 cups
1 quart (qt)	= 2 pints
1 gallon (gal)	= 4 quarts
1 liter (l)	= 1,000 milliliters (ml)

Measures of Time

1 minute (min)	= 60 seconds (sec)
1 hour (hr)	= 60 minutes
1 day	= 24 hours
1 week	= 7 days
1 year (yr)	= 365 days

Formulas

Perimeter (P) of a rectangle	$P = 2l + 2w$, where l is the length and w is the width
Area (A) of a rectangle	$A = lw$, where l is the length and w is the width
Volume (V) of a rectangular solid	$V = lwh$, where l is the length, w is the width, and h is the height
Circumference (C) of a circle	$C = \pi d$, where π is 3.14 or $\frac{22}{7}$ and d is the diameter
Area (A) of a circle	$A = \pi r^2$, where π is 3.14 or $\frac{22}{7}$ and r is the radius
Interest (i)	$i = prt$, where p is the principal, r is the rate, and t is the time

Glossary

A

addition   The mathematical operation used to find a sum. The problem $0.2 + 1.3 = 1.5$ is an example.

approximate   Another word for estimate. As an adjective: close or almost exact. The symbol $\approx$ means "is approximately equal to."

area   A measure of the amount of surface on a flat figure. A table top that is 6 feet long and 2.5 feet wide has an area of $6 \times 2.5 = 15$ square feet.

average   A sum divided by the number of items that make up the sum. An average, also called the *mean*, is a representative number for a group. If one package weighs 2.3 ounces and another weighs 4.5 ounces, their average weight is the sum $(2.3 + 4.5 = 6.8)$ divided by 2 (the number of packages). $6.8 \div 2 = 3.4$ ounces

B

borrowing   Regrouping the parts of the top number of a subtraction problem. In the problem $7 - 2\frac{3}{4}$, the 7 becomes $6\frac{4}{4}$.

C

canceling   Dividing a numerator in one fraction and a denominator in another fraction in a multiplication problem. For example, $\frac{2\cancel{4}}{5} \times \frac{1}{\cancel{6}_3} = \frac{2}{15}$

carrying   Regrouping the digits in an addition or multiplication problem. In the problem $2.6 + 1.9$, the sum of the tenths column is 15. The digit 5 remains in the tenths column, and the digit 1 is added to the units column.

circle   A flat figure for which every point is the same distance from the center.

circumference   A measure of the distance around a circle.

common denominator

common denominator   A number into which every denominator in a problem can divide evenly. For the problem $\frac{2}{3} + \frac{3}{4} + \frac{5}{6}$, the numbers 12, 24, and 36 are all common denominators.

consecutive   One after the other. The numbers 9 and 10 are consecutive; so are 20 and 21.

D

decimal   A fraction in which the whole is divided into tenths, hundredths, thousandths, ten-thousandths, and so on. The decimal $0.7 = \frac{7}{10}$.

decimal place   The position of a digit to the right of the decimal point. In the number 2.358, the digit 5 is in the hundredths place.

decimal point   A dot that separates whole numbers from decimal fractions. In the number 14.6, the point separates the whole number 14 from the decimal fraction $\frac{6}{10}$.

denominator   The bottom number or divisor in a fraction. In the fraction $\frac{3}{4}$, the denominator is 4.

diameter   The distance across a circle

difference   The answer to a subtraction problem. For the problem $2.9 - 0.5$, the difference is 2.4.

digit   One of the ten number symbols. The digits are 1, 2, 3, 4, 5, 6, 7, 8, 9, and 0.

dividend   The number in a division problem into which another number divides. In $6.8 \div 2 = 3.4$, the dividend is 6.8.

division   A mathematical operation that requires figuring out how many times one amount is contained in another. In the problem $\frac{3}{4} \div \frac{1}{8} = 6$, the answer means that there are exactly six one-eighths in $\frac{3}{4}$.

divisor   The number in a division problem that divides into another. In $4.5 \div 0.5 = 9$, the divisor is 0.5.

E

estimate   As a noun: an approximate value. For the problem $2\frac{7}{8} + 3\frac{8}{9}$, a reasonable estimate of an answer is 7. As a verb: to find an approximate value.

F

fixed-place accuracy   In a division problem, rounding an answer to a certain place. The division problem $2 \div 0.3$ never comes out even. To the nearest hundredth, the answer is 6.67.

formula   A mathematical rule written with an = sign. The formula for finding interest is $i = prt$, where i is the interest, p is the principal, r is the rate, and t is the time.

fraction   A part of a whole. The fraction $\frac{1}{4}$ tells what part a quarter is of a dollar. A fraction can also be thought of as a division problem. The fraction $\frac{6}{2}$ means six divided by two.

front-end rounding   Rounding the left-most digit of each number in a problem in order to calculate an estimate. In the problem 52×0.79, the number 52 rounds to 50 and 0.79 round to 0.8. The estimate is $50 \times 0.8 = 40$.

H

height   The straight-line measurement from the base of an object to the top. The measurements of a rectangular container include the length, the width, and the height.

higher terms   The opposite of the reduced form of a fraction. The fraction $\frac{3}{4}$ raised to twelfths is $\frac{9}{12}$.

I

improper fraction   A fraction in which the numerator is equal to or larger than the denominator. The fractions $\frac{5}{5}$ and $\frac{4}{3}$ are both improper fractions.

inequality   An expression that two amounts are not equal. The symbol < means *less than*. For example, $\frac{3}{8} < \frac{1}{2}$. The symbol > means *greater than*. For example, $\frac{5}{6} > \frac{1}{2}$.

interest   A charge for borrowing money, usually calculated as a percent of the money borrowed. For example, an 8% interest charge on $1,000 is $80.

invert   To reverse the position of the parts of a fraction. When the fraction $\frac{2}{3}$ is inverted, it becomes $\frac{3}{2}$.

K

kilogram   The standard unit of weight in the metric system. A kilogram is a little more than two pounds.

L

label   A word or abbreviation used to identify the unit of measurement of some quantity. An envelope has a weight in ounces. The label is ounces.

liter   The standard unit of liquid measure in the metric system. A liter is about the same as one quart.

lowest common denominator   The lowest number into which every denominator in a problem can divide evenly. For the problem $\frac{5}{6} + \frac{3}{4}$, the lowest common denominator is 12.

lowest terms   The most reduced form of a fraction. The fraction $\frac{16}{20}$ reduced to lowest terms is $\frac{4}{5}$.

M

mean   Another word for average. A sum divided by the number of items that make up the sum.

measurement   A dimension, quantity, or capacity. The measurements of a room usually include the length, the width, and the height.

meter   The standard unit of length in the metric system. A meter is a little more than one yard.

metric system   A standard of measure based on tens, hundreds, and thousands. The standard unit of length in the metric system is the meter. The standard unit of weight is the kilogram. The standard unit of liquid measure is the liter.

mixed decimal   A number with both a whole number and a decimal fraction. In the mixed decimal 4.3, the whole number is 4 and the decimal fraction is 3 tenths.

mixed number A number with both a whole number and a fraction. For example, $5\frac{1}{2}$ is a mixed number.

multiplication A mathematical operation with whole numbers that consists of adding a number a certain number of times. For example, the problem $4 \times 3 = 12$ means finding the sum of three fours: $4 + 4 + 4 = 12$. With fractions, multiplication means finding a *part* of another number. For example, the problem $\frac{1}{3} \times 15 = 5$ means finding a third of fifteen.

N

numerator The top number in a fraction. In the fraction $\frac{2}{9}$, the numerator is 2.

O

operation A mathematical process such as addition, subtraction, multiplication, or division

P

parallel Being an equal distance apart. The sides opposite each other in a rectangle are parallel.

percent One hundredth or $\frac{1}{100}$. The symbol % means percent. An entire amount is 100%. Half of an entire amount is 50%.

perimeter A measure of the distance around a flat figure. A rectangle that is 5 meters long and 2.5 meters wide has a perimeter of 15 meters.

place value The number that every digit stands for. In the number 26.8, the digit 2 stands for 20 because 2 is in the tens place. The digit 8 stands for $\frac{8}{10}$ because 8 is in the tenths place.

principal The amount of money on which interest is calculated.

product The answer to a multiplication problem. For the problem $3.4 \times 2 = 6.8$, the product is 6.8.

proper fraction A fraction in which the numerator (the top number) is less than the denominator (the bottom number). The fractions $\frac{8}{9}$ and $\frac{1}{500}$ are both proper fractions.

Q

quotient The answer to a division problem. In the problem $8.2 \div 2 = 4.1$, the quotient is 4.1.

R

radius Half the diameter of a circle. Also, the distance from the center of the circle to any point on the circle

rate An amount whose unit of measure contains a word such as *per* or *for each*. For example, the speed (or rate of speed) of a moving vehicle is often measured in *miles per hour*. Interest is measured in *percent*.

reciprocal The inverse of a fraction. $\frac{4}{5}$ is the reciprocal of $\frac{5}{4}$.

rectangle A four-sided figure with four square corners. A page of a textbook is a rectangle.

rectangular solid A three-dimensional figure such as a box that has length, width, and height

reducing Expressing a fraction with smaller numbers. The fraction $\frac{9}{18}$ can be reduced to $\frac{1}{2}$. The reduced form of a fraction has the same value as the original form.

rounding Making an estimate that is close to an original amount. 4.862 rounded to the nearest tenth is 4.9.

S

square A four-sided flat figure with four right angles and four equal sides.

subtraction The mathematical operation used to find the difference between two numbers. The problem $\frac{5}{8} - \frac{4}{8} = \frac{1}{8}$ is an example.

sum The answer to an addition problem. The sum of 0.3 and 0.4 is 0.7.

symbol A printed sign that represents an operation, a quantity, or a relationship. The symbol + means to add. The symbol ° means degree. The symbol < means less than.

T

time A measurement from a point in the past to a more recent point. The units of measurement for time are seconds, minutes, hours, days, weeks, months, years, and so on.

total Another word for sum; the answer to an addition problem

U

units of measurement Labels for determining a quantity. For example, pounds and kilograms are units of measurement for weight.

unit The name of the right-most place in a whole number. In the number 36.2051, the digit 6 is in the units place.

V

volume The amount of space occupied by a three-dimensional object. A rectangular box that is 4 feet long, 3 feet wide, and $\frac{1}{2}$ foot high has a volume of 6 cubic feet.

W

whole number A number that can be divided evenly by 1. For example, 2 and 30 and 1,000 are all whole numbers.

Z

zero The mathematical symbol 0. A fraction in which the numerator is much smaller than the denominator is close to 0 in value. For example, the fraction $\frac{1}{99}$ is much closer to 0 than the fraction $\frac{98}{99}$.

Index

Wright Group

ISBN: 0-8092-2377-5

Send all inquiries to:
Wright Group/McGraw-Hill
130 E. Randolph, Suite 400
Chicago, IL 60601

Printed in the United States of America.

11 12 13 14 15 16 VHG 08 07 06

The **McGraw·Hill** Companies

**Fractions, Decimals,
and Percents**

Contemporary's

Number Power

a real world approach to math

Jerry Howett

McGraw Hill   Wright Group